BAR CODE ON BACK PAGE

D&T CHALLENGES

DESIGN & TECHNOLOGY 11-14

SCHOOLS

In association with the
CHANNEL 4 SCHOOLS series
Real Life Design

A TC Trust programme sponsored and
supported by the Royal College of Art,
the Esmée Fairbairn Trust,
Garfield Weston Foundation and the
Department for Education and Employment

Hodder & Stoughton

A MEMBER OF THE HODDER HEADLINE GROUP

Acknowledgements

The publishers would like to thank the following:

Danny Jenkins of fab 4 studio for the cover illustration; Lynda King for the cover and book design; Helene Rogers for picture research; Sally Artz, Maggie Brand, Bill Donohoe, Phil Ford, Susan Hutchinson and Joe McEwan for the illustrations.

We are also grateful to the following companies, agencies and individuals who have given permission to reproduce photos and artwork in this book. Every effort has been made to trace and acknowledge ownership of copyright. The publishers will be glad to make suitable arrangements with any copyright holder whom it has not been possible to contact.

Advertising Archives (36 top left); Alida Packaging Ltd (33 bottom left); BFI Stills, Posters and Designs (18 top, 50 middle right); © John Birdsall (77 both bottom, 86 top and middle left, 120); courtesy CarnaudMetalbox Aerosols (UK) PLC (123 bottom right); © Crafts Council (40 left, 42 top, 45 bottom right); © Dargaud Editeur 1973, Goscinny-Uderzo/Hodder and Stoughton Ltd 1980 (18 bottom); Design Age (102 bottom left); Döhler (UK) Ltd (77 top, 100); Emil Kemper GMBH (13 top); Gill Greaney (43 both); Greenhalgh's Craft Bakery Ltd (6 left); Maggie Grey (45 middle right, 87, 88 all); courtesy of IBM (114 both); © Mick Inkpen (14 top right, 18 middle); LSG/Sky Chefs (71 top, 74 all); Patricia Moore (103 both bottom); Museum of Automata, York (49 left); New Holland (45 middle left); Ogilvy and Maither (36 top right);

Robin Pellatt (22 middle right); © Tanya Piejus, courtesy of PC World and Rodney Fitch and Co. (107 middle and bottom right); Thames and Hudson (56 all right, 57, 58 all; 59 top right and bottom left); © TRIP/Aquablade (80 bottom); © TRIP/J Booth (79); © TRIP/Dyson (59 bottom middle); © TRIP/G Fleming (62 bottom); © TRIP/B Gibbs (124 bottom right); © TRIP/Ibrahim (122 bottom right); © TRIP/V Greaves (65); © TRIP/HHCL (37 middle); © TRIP/G Howe (40 centre right); © TRIP/W Jacobs (78 middle); © TRIP/M Lee (47, 78 top); © TRIP/J Moscrop (51 top left); © TRIP/Nissan (46, 51 top right); © TRIP/J Okwesa (49 bottom right, 124 bottom left); © TRIP/P Rauter (62 top); © TRIP/H Rogers (7, 8, 10 both, 11, 13 bottom, 14 left and bottom right, 17 bottom, 19 both, 20, 21 top, 22 all, 23, 26, 28, 29, 31 both, 32 all except bottom left, 33 all, 34 both, 35, 36 bottom, 37 top and bottom, 40 top right, bottom right, 42 bottom, 44 both, 45 top, bottom left and middle, 49 top and middle right, 50 middle left, 51 all bottom, 52, 53, 59 top left, 63, 64 all, 67 both, 69 both, 70 all left, 71, 78 bottom, 80 top right, 81, 86 middle right and bottom, 90, 94 both, 98 all, 99, 103 both top, 104 all, 105 top, 106 all, 107 all left and both top right, 108 all, 109 all, 110, 113 top right, 116 all, 117 both, 118 both, 119 all, 122 all except bottom right, 123 both top, 125); © TRIP/N Price (41 top); © TRIP/Barry Salter (83 left); © TRIP/Eric Smith (59 bottom right); © TRIP/Tel Marketing (83 right); © TRIP/B Turner (59 top left); © TRIP/TRIP (17 top, 21 bottom, 56 left, 61 both, 105 bottom, 112 both, 113 both bottom); © TRIP/Y Varigin (41 bottom); © TRIP/Westlight (80 left); © Stewart Weir (124 top); Winpenny Photography (30).

Cataloguing in Publication Data is available from the British Library

ISBN 0 340 639296

First published 1997

Impression number	10	9	8	7	6	5	4	3	2	1
Year	2000	1999	1998	1997						

Typeset by Wearset, Boldon, Tyne and Wear.
Printed in Great Britain for Hodder & Stoughton Educational, a division of Hodder Headline PLC, 338 Euston Road, London NW1 3BH by Bath Colour Books, Glasgow.

ROYAL COLLEGE OF ART SCHOOLS TECHNOLOGY PROJECT

The Royal College of Art Schools Technology Project began in September 1993. It is designed to raise the sights and cater for the curricular needs of technology teachers in secondary schools. The project is funded by the Esmée Fairbairn Charitable Trust, Garfield Western Foundation, Cable and Wireless plc and the Department for Education and Employment.

The underlying purpose is to improve the quality of technology education throughout secondary schools in England.

The Project's central team is based at the Royal College of Art, supporting developments in 13 selected secondary schools with Teacher Fellows on part-time secondment. They are developing a comprehensive design and technology course for students aged 11 to 19. The whole team is working closely with business organisations and major industrial companies to ensure a curriculum that is relevant to the worlds of business and commerce.

This student book forms part of the course developed to deliver the requirements of, and to enhance, the National Curriculum and post-14 work, particularly for GNVQ.

Royal College of Art Schools Technology Project 1996 Writing Team

Teacher Fellows and Partner Schools
Alan Booth (Wymondham College, Norfolk)
Claire Buxton (City and Islington College, London)
Anne Constable (Beauchamp College, Leicester)
Corinne Harper (Burntwood School for Girls, London)
Mark Hudson (Bishop Fox's Community College, Somerset)
Dai James (Ashfield School, Nottinghamshire)
Mary Moran (Kingsway School, Cheadle)
Barbara Mottershead (Shevington High School, Wigan)
Robin Pellatt (Bishop David Brown School, Woking)
Rob Petrie (Exeter St Thomas High School, Devon)
Brian Russell (Dixons CTC, Bradford)
Kalvin Turner (Bosworth Community College, Leicester)

Project Team
David Perry – Project Director
Louise T Davies – Deputy Project Director
Antony R Booth – Assistant Project Director
Jim Sage – Assistant Project Director
Vicki Fentiman, Doris Massiah – Project Assistants

Acknowledgements

Our special thanks to all of the Teacher Fellows and their schools and particularly their colleagues, partners, friends and children who have supported them whilst they were writing to meet all the deadlines. The Royal College of Art Schools Technology Project wishes to extend its thanks to the following for their support and help in the writing of this book – Kathleen Lund (Chief Executive) and her colleagues at the Technology Colleges Trust, The Department for Education and Employment, the Office for Standards in Education (OFSTED), the Royal College of Art, and their representatives on the Project Management Group: many thanks to Corinne Harper and Robin Pellatt for leading the Y9 team and co-ordinating the writing of the Y9 work so effectively. Special thanks to Gill Greaney for writing the Fantasy Headwear Challenge; Josephine Dyer, Tricia Collins, Roger Crabtree of George Ward School, Ruth Conway, Terry Fiehn, Maggie and Clive Grey, Lesley Cresswell, Janet Inglis for their written contributions; Geoff White, St Helier Safety Ltd; Prof R Thomas Wright, Ball State University, Indiana; Graham Lane, Bulldog Buckle Co; Naser Iqbal, Dixons CTC; Belinda Downes; Michael Diesendorff, Husqvarna; David Letherman, LSG/Sky Chefs; Kim Field, Volker Hellwig and Christina Chan, Royal College of Art; Steve Crawford, Pennine Foods; John Myerson, Richmond LEA; Speedo; Nick Lowe, Dixons Plc; Mike Baxter, Alida Packaging Ltd; Geoff Widdup, Widdup and Sons; Barrie Kemp, Greenhalgh Craft Bakery Ltd; G Anderton, Tom Chandley Ovens; Kay Nicholls, Mars; Graham Parker and Pat Chown, United Biscuits; Chris Phillips, Ross Young; Bruce Toon and Athol Bruce, Döhler (UK) Ltd; The Charnley Arms, Standish, Wigan; Andy Roberts, Freelance Animatronics Designer; Bill Emmerich, Emmerich Berlon Ltd; Atkinson Design Associates; Design Age, Royal College of Art; Patricia Moore, Guyner Design Inc, Arizona; Fitch and Co; Phillip Allen Publishers Ltd; Loughborough University; The Boots Co Plc; Avon Technical Products; Clark's International.

Contents

Welcome to D&T Challenges!

This book has two sections. At the front of the book you will find 12 Challenges. Towards the back of the book you will find a section on Designing and Manufacturing. This section will help you with all of the Challenges. Turn to this section when you need help with a problem:

- How can I find out about designing for clients and designing for manufacture?
- What do I need to think about when I am designing?
- How can I use graphics in my designing?
- How will looking at existing products help me to design better?
- How can I plan the making of my product?
- How can I make sure that my product is of good quality?

This section will give you help and information. Try some of the activities in this section to develop your designing and making skills. You can also try these at home or if you have some spare time at the end of a project.

Your Challenges

You will probably not have time to do all 12 Challenges, but your teacher will pick a course made up of those that are best for your class. All the Challenges ask you to design and make things. You will use all sorts of materials and components, including food, textiles, plastics, wood, metal and electronics.

Over the year you will improve the quality of the products you design and make. Your work will get better and more complex. You will be designing for people and situations that are less familiar to you. You will have to research and test your design carefully to develop better products. Throughout this book you will find examples of designing and making from the adult world. Try to improve your work until it becomes more like these examples. Often you will be asked to design products that can be made in large volumes, and the examples shown in the book of how this is done in industry will help you to do this better.

As you begin to prepare for Year 10 examination courses, you will be expected to work more independently. Use the Challenges and activities to help you plan your work by yourself and with your classmates. Use the designing and making section of this book when you have problems and need to make decisions.

You will also be working in a team. Practise being a good team member – this will help you now and later in life.

The twelve activities

You will see the following headings in each project. What do they mean?

Your Challenge   Each activity is introduced with a Challenge. Your teacher will introduce the project and plan it with you. Try to look ahead as this will help you to plan your own projects by yourself later. There are important pictures on the page which will help your designing and making.

Why this activity is useful   Each project has been included in this book for a good reason. This box will tell you what important skills and ideas you are going to learn.

The broader picture . . .   Each Challenge provokes important questions. When we are designing and making products this affects other people, the environment and so on. Your teacher may discuss these questions with your class, you may like to answer them for homework, or find out more about something that is important to you. How do these issues affect your designing?

To be successful   Check this box often as it will help you to do well in each project. You can also use this to help you to evaluate how well you have done at the end of the project.

Planning things through   You can't depend on your teacher to do everything for you. You should take some responsibility for planning your own work. These are important hints and tips for you.

Baker's dozen

Your challenge!

A bread manufacturer is concerned that bread in general does not appeal to young people. The manufacturer has asked the Design and Technology students in your school to investigate and design a new bread product aimed at young people. **Your challenge** is to present a prototype of your design and to think about how the bread will be produced on a larger scale. You may try out **batch production** methods with a group in your class. An important feature of this bread product is that it contributes to a healthy diet.

Why this activity is useful

Bread is a fun product to work with. There are so many different products you can make – the sky's your limit!

◆ You will design a new bread product for a target group of consumers.

◆ You will find out about the nutritional value of bread products.

◆ You learn about the origins of bread.

◆ You will discover how bread products are designed and manufactured.

◆ You will find out about the effects that the ingredients and processes used have on the bread.

◆ You will learn about the differences between making one item and large quantities of the same item.

The broader picture . . .

◆ Interview a person over 40 years old about what bread was available when they were young. How is it different from the bread that you eat?

◆ Why are people willing to pay a great deal more for a speciality bread than an ordinary loaf?

◆ Why is bread sometimes called 'the staff of life'?

To be successful

★ You will design and make a high quality new bread product that appeals to young people and will make them want to eat more bread.

★ You will investigate how you can achieve different effects, tastes and textures with bread.

★ The item will be suitable for high volume production.

★ You will produce a thorough, well presented record of your research, plans, ideas and actions in your design portfolio.

Planning things through

❱ Investigate existing bread products thoroughly.

❱ Leave time to find out about the preferences and opinions of people in your target group.

❱ You will need to allow time to develop and trial prototypes of your new bread ideas with your target group.

❱ An action plan or GANNT chart will help you to plan your time.

❱ Don't forget that your final idea must be suitable for manufacturing in high volume.

Understanding the market for bread and bread products

What is 'bread'? Does it always have yeast in it? Is it always baked in the oven? Is it savoury or sweet? How many breads can you think of? How many other products are made from a bread mixture or dough?

How can you come up with a new idea that will be liked by your target group? Here are some ideas:

■ **Eat some bread.** Carry out a survey and/or taste panel of bread products already available in the shops. Who are they aimed at? Are any products aimed at your target group and what are they like? What are the main ingredients? How much do they cost? How are they made?

■ **Hunt the label!** Look at the labels of different breads for an assessment of their nutritional value. How can you make your bread healthy to eat?

■ **Look for something special.** Identify where 'new' breads have come from. For example, why are people eating more Italian breads?

■ **Get busy on the Internet or get hold of some books.** Research breads traditional to different cultures or countries, or kinds of bread made many years ago. Could you develop an idea that might interest your target group? You will find a lot of information in recipe books, but do not be afraid to experiment with something new.

■ **Get trendy!** Find out about trends in eating bread and other products. What is the most popular type of bread in Britain and why? Which types of bread are increasing or declining in their sales? Think of reasons for these changes.

Designing for your target group

Who are they? How are you going to find out what your target group would like?

You will need to carry out some research to find out about your target group. You must use this research to help you identify which ideas will be the most successful.

A spider diagram is a useful way to show what people like

what are their preferences – taste, colour, texture?

how much will they spend?

how big should it be?

what are their individual needs?

fashion themes

what will young people like?

what are their favourite ingredients?

interests

when do they eat bread?

images

Designing for a healthy diet

You have been asked to design a bread that contributes to a healthy diet for young people. The Department of Health recommends that we eat at least four slices of bread every day. Find out why bread can contribute to a healthy diet.

Does your target group eat enough bread to meet these guidelines? How can they be encouraged to eat more bread?

Use a database on a computer or food tables to analyse the nutritional value of recipe ideas.

Finding out about ingredients

Understanding the ingredients will help you to design and make your bread. The best way to do this is by carrying out some practical research. Bread can be changed by the ingredients you use, and by the way you cook it, shape it and finish it.

You might try to:

■ bake bread with different types of flour

■ add different ingredients such as sugar, milk, fruit or butter to a bread dough

■ use different types of yeast

■ use different cooking methods.

For all of these tests you can compare the results using a variety of techniques, such as:

■ run a taste panel

■ look at texture by making prints

■ measuring the size of the dough before and after cooking.

Remember: working as a group and sharing results speeds up this sort of work.

Trying different things

Using different flours

Where does flour come from? What kind of bread can you make with each type of flour?

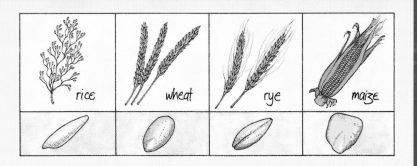

rice   wheat   rye   maize

Trying different things (continued)

Using yeast

Is bread always made with yeast? What does the yeast do? Which sort helps you to manufacture bread quickest? How much do you need to use? How much does each cost? Which tastes do your clients like best?

Trying different shapes

How long does each take? Which dough is best? Which is easiest to make? Which is easiest to make identically? How evenly do they cook? Which do your clients prefer?

Adding different ingredients

What other ingredients can be added to the bread mixture? How do they affect colour, flavour, texture, keeping qualities? Which tastes do your clients prefer?

Using different finishes

What differences do various finishes make to the crust and appearance?

Comparing cooking methods

What differences does cooking method make to the appearance and taste?
How long does each take?

Baking with yeast

The picture shows what happens when bread is baked. Identify all the words that you do not understand. Work in a group to find out what they mean. Explain to each other, in your own words, what happens when bread is baked.

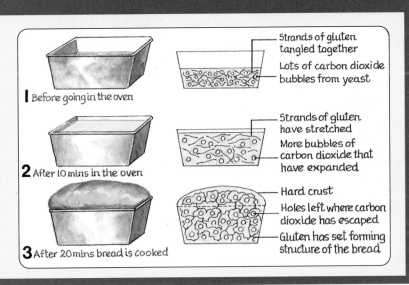

1 Before going in the oven

Strands of gluten tangled together

Lots of carbon dioxide bubbles from yeast

2 After 10 mins in the oven

Strands of gluten have stretched

More bubbles of carbon dioxide that have expanded

3 After 20 mins bread is cooked

Hard crust

Holes left where carbon dioxide has escaped

Gluten has set forming structure of the bread

Case study – 'Just in time' manufacturing

Barrie Kemp tells us how the Greenhalgh Craft Bakery Ltd investigated using a new type of dough.

'Yeast just keeps rising and rising until you bake the bread and the yeast is killed. This is a real problem for an in-store bakery who want to provide fresh bread for their customers. They want to be able to make a large batch of dough, and then leave it to one side and cook it when they need it. You cannot leave the bread to keep on rising as it 'overproves' and is inedible.

'With the use of additives, a special dough can be made which means the dough can be left for much longer before baking. This means that there is less waste for the manufacturer and more fresh bread for the consumer. This saves money and makes the bread cheaper.'

Making bread on a larger scale

You now have a prototype that you have tested on a small scale by making it in small quantities. If your product is going to be manufactured you need to think about designing for manufacture in larger quantities.

Perhaps you can try making a larger volume with your class mates. This is called **scaling up**. It will give you an idea of what the problems might be.

Things to think about

■ Can the mixture be made in bulk?

■ Is your recipe as simple as possible?

■ Are the raw ingredients readily available?

■ How long does it take?

■ How much complex preparation and hand-finishing is required?

■ Can any processes be done by machine?

■ How much wastage will there be?

■ How reliable is your 'recipe' and process? Does it come out the same each time? What can you do to make sure that it does?

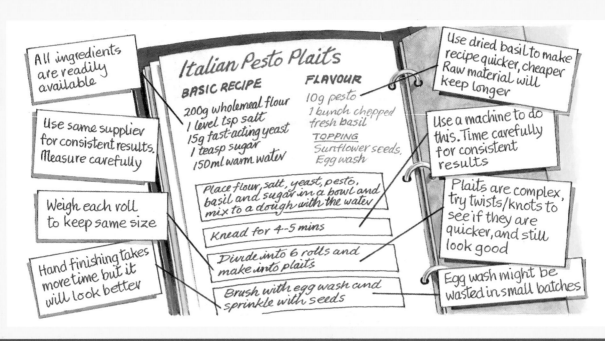

All ingredients are readily available

Use same supplier for consistent results. Measure carefully

Weigh each roll to keep same size

Hand finishing takes more time but it will look better

Italian Pesto Plaits

BASIC RECIPE
200g wholemeal flour
1 level tsp salt
15g fast-acting yeast
1 teasp sugar
150ml warm water

FLAVOUR
10g pesto
1 bunch chopped fresh basil
TOPPING
Sunflower seeds,
Egg wash

Place flour, salt, yeast, pesto, basil and sugar in a bowl and mix to a dough with the water

Knead for 4-5 mins

Divide into 6 rolls and make into plaits

Brush with egg wash and sprinkle with seeds

Use dried basil to make recipe quicker, cheaper Raw material will keep longer

Use a machine to do this. Time carefully for consistent results

Plaits are complex, try twists/knots to see if they are quicker, and still look good

Egg wash might be wasted in small batches

Getting it right

Designing and Manufacturing:
Thinking about volumes   123
of production

It is important when producing large quantities of bread that the finished product meets a specified standard. All the bread rolls produced should be the same in terms of size and weight, shape, taste and appearance.

How does a manufacturer make sure that its bread is all the same?

Work in a team to complete the following task:

Produce a batch of rolls that are all of identical size, shape and appearance. You can use a commercial bread mix so that you are carrying out a fair test and saving time.

1 Look at the instructions on the pack.
2 Plan what you are going to do carefully. If you divide out the tasks be sure that everyone in the team has a useful job.
3 Make and bake your bread rolls.
4 Did they all come out the same? What techniques did you try? Which ones were most successful?

Redesign the instructions on the packet into a flow diagram and add extra information on how to get the rolls all the same.

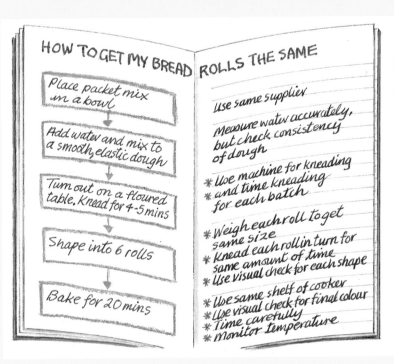

HOW TO GET MY BREAD ROLLS THE SAME

Place packet mix in a bowl
↓
Add water and mix to a smooth, elastic dough
↓
Turn out on a floured table. Knead for 4-5 mins
↓
Shape into 6 rolls
↓
Bake for 20 mins

Use same supplier

Measure water accurately, but check consistency of dough

* Use machine for kneading
* and time kneading for each batch

* Weigh each roll to get same size
* Knead each roll in turn for same amount of time
* Use visual check for each shape

* Use same shelf of cooker
* Use visual check for final colour
* Time carefully
* Monitor temperature

What are the advantages and disadvantages of using a team of people during production?

In food manufacturing, **unit processes** is the term used to describe the different jobs

Stories for children

Your challenge!

Young children love books and the more unusual, exciting and original the better. The possibilities are endless. There are hundreds on the market and more appear every week. Many of these are old favourites coming out in new versions with new illustrations.

Your challenge is to design and produce a storybook for a child of your choice. You should think about their age and interests and carry out some research to find out what they really want from a book.

Your storybook could be made in a variety of ways. It could be a traditional paper and card book, or a fabric book. It could be a book designed on a computer using computer graphics and animation.

Why this activity is useful

- ◆ This is an opportunity to design and make something for a particular client.

- ◆ You will learn how to write a client profile and test your product on a real person.

- ◆ There will be opportunities to be very creative.

- ◆ You will learn more about graphic design materials and media.

- ◆ You will develop graphical skills.

- ◆ You will appreciate the relationship between art and design more.

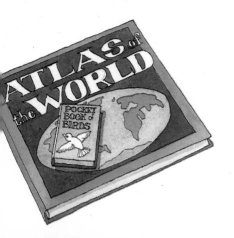

The broader picture . . .

◆ Why is story-telling so enjoyable for young children?

◆ Why do some books offend people? Think about 'stereotypical' images. How do you feel about these images?

◆ Will computers replace books?

◆ When powerful dictators ban or burn books people get very upset. Why do you think this is?

To be successful

You will:

★ show that you fully understand your client and his or her requirements

★ carry out thorough research to find out about the range of children's books available

★ make sure that you have an interesting storyline and plot, 'colourful' characters, and colourful and appropriate visuals

★ produce a well-made, professionally-finished book

★ successfully test your book on a suitable child or group of children

★ have a clear record of how you designed your book, why it ended up as it did and what else you considered along the way.

Planning things through

▶ Check what is available for you to use: materials, computers, other equipment, time, etc.

▶ Discuss with your teacher how ambitious you can be.

▶ Remember to plan out the whole book – writing, illustrations, etc. – before you start to produce the final copy. Using a storyboard will help you to do this.

▶ Allocate time for testing it with your client.

Evaluating existing children's books

As a class, make a collection of as many children's books as you can. In groups, compare the books and decide what you think makes 'a good children's book'. Make lists to show the good and bad points.

Rewrite your list with the most important points at the top and least important at the bottom.

Developing a client profile

Books are often written for particular children and situations. For example, a book may be made for a young child who is going into hospital, or for a child who is afraid of the dark. In groups, write down other situations or circumstances when children might need special books.

You will need to find out what is appropriate for the age of your chosen client. Your school librarian may be able to help. You could also contact a local nursery or playgroup and talk to people who care for young children.

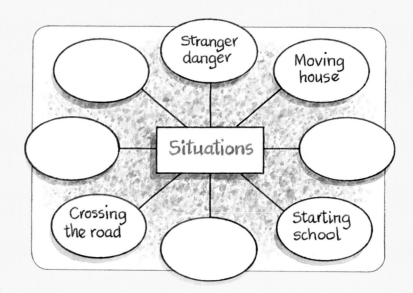

Look closely at examples of books that have been written for your chosen age group. What do they reveal about the designers' ideas of what children of this age like, want and need in books?

Find some children who fit your client group to talk to about books. Find out what they like. What makes books interesting for them? Do they read their books or have books read to them, or both? Do they look at the pictures first or read the text?

What is possible? Ways of telling stories

Think about the different ways to tell a story, e.g. photostories and audio tapes. Note down as many as you can. Your teacher may give you a chart to help with this.

Try sketching some ideas of your own. Could the book have alternative endings?

Case study – fabric books

Fabric books are more textural than printed paper books. Members of the Young Textiles Group (Embroiderers Guild) decided to make a fairy tale book for visually impaired children.

After considering the client profile and carrying out research with the Royal National Institute for the Blind, they made the following design decisions:

- There should be a variety of textures
- There must be Braille headings that the children could read

- The design of each page must be clear
- Common features must be the same on each page.

The storyboard was created using pieces of paper to represent different types of

fabric such as silk, leather, velvet, net, lace and brocade. Experiments with paint produced raised lettering for Braille headings, and trials with folding paper and stitching provided an effective binding system for the book.

Initial ideas

Novelties

Think about novelty books that would appeal to your client group. These might be things like pop-up books, ones that make a noise, or have moving parts like flaps, laces or buttons.

Developing your book

Preparing the story – storyboarding

The story is the most important part of the book. Work out your ideas about the story before you make too many other decisions about the book. You could use a storyboard to help you. This means drawing sketches in small boxes to show the sequence of the story. This is how films are planned.

This can help you to write the text, as you can plan how many words and how much of the story will fit on each page.

You will then have to write a draft of the story. You should test it on children of the right age to make sure that it is appropriate.

Developing the characters

Characters make the story come to life. You need to think hard about this.

- Who are they?
- Are they ordinary people, or maybe animals?
- What are they like?
- How do they behave?
- What do they do?
- How do they look?

Young children like animal characters. These are from *Kipper's Book of Counting* by Mick Inkpen

Illustrations

Illustrations are also very important. Use your research to help you to develop the illustration style in your book. Will you use cartoons, comic strip, photographs, line drawings or black and white sketches?

Remember to think about what is most appropriate for your characters and for your client.

A strip cartoon from *Asterix in Corsica*

Developing your book (continued)

The format
How big, what shape?

The format and layout of your storybook should be appropriate for the age and size of the client. Perhaps you can make it look unusual!

Maybe you could design a book like one of these

Materials

Now consider the different materials you could use. Start to think about how you can actually make your book and write a list of what you will need.

You might want to glue layers of material together (**laminating**). Does your school have a laminating machine? Can you get some transparent or coloured book-covering film? Could you glue paper pages to card for stiffness?

Equipment

What equipment can you use? Are you able to use a computer to help you with word-processing or drawing?

Can you use a sewing machine, embroidery machine or plotter cutter?

What can you use to save time when making repeating features, such as the borders on each page?

Using multimedia

ADD "BUTTONS" FOR AN INTERACTIVE STORY

ADD MUSIC AND SONGS

ADD SOUND EFFECTS FOR ATMOSPHERE

ADD SPEECH USING A MICROPHONE

WRITE YOUR OWN STORY USING DTP

ADD MOVING VIDEO IMAGES AND CARTOONS

SCAN IN PHOTOS

DRAW YOUR OWN PICTURES

If you have access to a multimedia computer system you can design and make a very exciting 'computer book'

Planning your making

To plan the book in detail you will need to complete the storyboard of the whole book. Try to show as much detail as possible in your sketches and add annotations about anything that cannot be shown in the drawings.

Red book:
Drawing your ideas   98

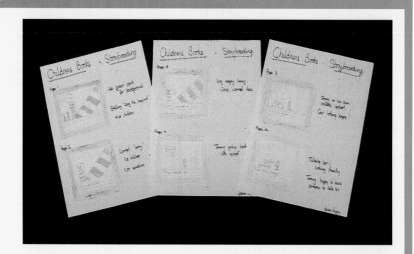

Planning your making (continued)

Plan your book page by page. Use your storyboard to produce full page **roughs**. These are sketches (not finished drawings) of what the pages will look like at full size. Include all illustrations and text.

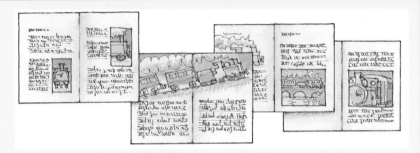

Produce a rough

Add covers and anything else you need to the roughs and you will have a complete **mock-up** of your book to test before making your final version.

The mock-up and finished versions of a student's book design

Testing and evaluating your book

■ How are you going to test your book?

■ When will be the best time to ask people for their opinions?

■ Where will you do this?

■ Who will you ask – the child, parents, teachers, carers?

■ Is your client too young to ask directly?

■ How will you organise the tests?

■ How much time will the child have with the book?

■ Can you record some of the test on video or on audio tape?

Playgroup leaders or parents could then help you to judge how well the book worked with your client child. You could also use the tape to show your teacher for assessment.

How will you know if your book is successful? Look back through your planning and check the *To be successful* box on page 15.

Buckling up!

Your challenge!

We sometimes need to fasten things. Toe-clips on bicycles, buckles used to strap bikes to the back of cars, quick release straps on bags, safety harnesses for young children, rock climbing equipment, and a chin-strap for a riding hat are some of the many examples.

Your challenge is to design and make a product to meet a fastening need. You should design your fastening device so that it can be manufactured in quantity, rather than only made once.

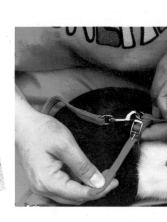

Why this activity is useful

You will soon be able to answer these questions more fully:

◆ How are small items like buckles and fasterners produced cheaply and in quantity so that they are all the same?

◆ What do designers need to take into account when designing products for high volumes of production?

◆ What kinds of materials and processes are most suitable when many identical products have to be made?

You can also use many of your existing skills to help with this Challenge.

The broader picture . . .

Discuss in a group a number of fastening devices that are primarily designed to ensure safety (e.g. those on safety belts or children's reins). In each case, explain how the mechanism works that ensures safety in the worst case scenario (e.g. holding a safety belt in a crash, but also allowing an adult to release it quickly, while preventing a child releasing it at will).

How would a device that could be fastened and released by someone with arthritic fingers be different from one that you would use?

To be successful

You will need to:

★ research why your fastening will be needed and the specific requirements it will have to meet to provide a safe and effective fastener

★ understand what kind of grip it needs to give

★ show how it could be made in quantity and of consistent quality

★ test your design in use. It should work well, including doing it up and undoing it. Make improvements to the design and manufacture of the product

★ consider how many people might want to buy it, or the kind of products it might be used in.

Planning things through

Research different kinds of fasteners and record your findings using sketches and notes.

Find out what materials, machines and tools are available to you in school. You will also need to think about:

▸ what kind of fastening your users will need

▸ how to make more than one identical product

▸ how to make sure that you can work accurately.

Investigating fasteners – how do we 'belt up'?

One of the most commonly used fasteners is a buckle on a belt.

The belt works by threading the loose end into the frame and putting the pin into one of the holes. When the loose end is pulled tight the pin falls against the frame and so stops the belt coming undone

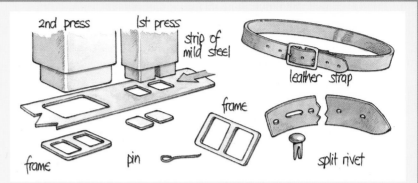

You should use sketches and notes to illustrate your work

To help your own designing you need to know more about fasteners. Carry out an investigation into different fasteners, recording your results in a chart. As a class you may divide up the work and each look at different types of fasteners and then share your research.

Here are some things you might like to find out:

■ What is its function?

■ How is it made?

■ Why was it designed like this?

■ How does the manufacturing method influence the design?

Special fasteners and their design attributes

Why do you think so many fasteners are needed on this product?

Some types of fasteners are designed to work in a special way to meet a particular need. The picture opposite is of a child's harness. It is made from woven nylon straps with metal and plastic buckles. In total it has sixteen buckles, some of which are the same. Apart from the quick release side and rear buckles they are all pressed from mild steel sheet.

What special needs will your fastener have to meet?

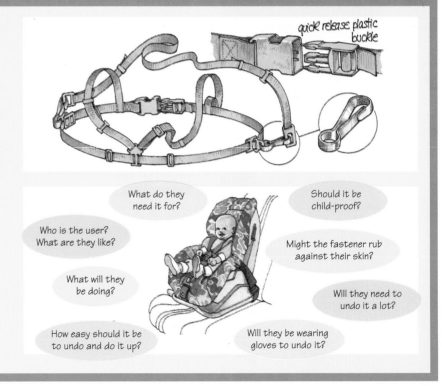

Special fasteners and their design attributes (continued)

Fasteners use friction to help them grip. You will need to decide how to get grip when you design your fastener. Before you begin making a prototype, you could experiment with different materials, surfaces and designs to get a good grip.

the two materials. eg: strap–the woven material provides a rough surface to increase friction

the force pushing the surfaces together. eg: when the strap and buckle are used. they are pulled apart like this. This increases the amount of friction.

the type of surface on each material– eg: the rough surface on this buckle increases the friction.

Three factors that affect the amount of friction

Manufacturing methods used in school

Some methods will be better for manufacturing your fastening in quantity. These methods may be available for you to use in your school. Investigate which will be the best method for your fastener and produce a plan for making your fastener in quantity. Remember that it is very important to be able to make each fastener to a set quality. If your fastener has a safety function, the fastener must not fail because it is badly made. Every one made has to perform well. How can you guarantee this?

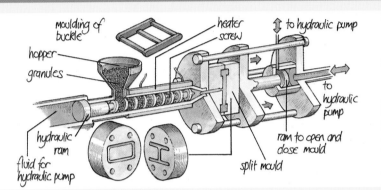

moulding of buckle
hopper
granules
hydraulic ram
fluid for hydraulic pump
heater
screw
to hydraulic pump
to hydraulic pump
ram to open and close mould
split mould

During injection moulding hot plastic is driven or injected into a 'split mould'. Shapes are formed in the mould cavity and can be released when it is pulled apart. Why will every product be the same shape?

Injection moulding

This process is used to heat plastic, which is then injected by force into a mould or cavity.

If you do not have an injection moulding machine in your school you may still be able to improvise.

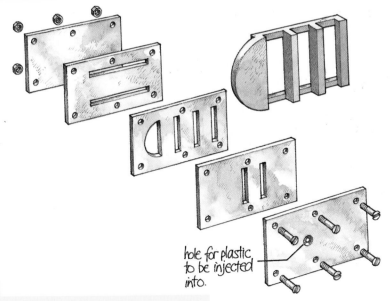

hole for plastic to be injected into.

Layering can be used as a substitute for injection moulding

Designing and Manufacturing: Injection moulding 121

Manufacturing methods used in school (continued)

Casting

Liquid or molten material is tipped into a mould. Sometimes pressure is used to make sure that the liquid completely fills up the space before it solidifies to make the desired shape.

Designing and Manufacturing: Casting 121

Sand can be used to make moulds for hot, liquid metal. The mould is then broken up to remove the casting. Is there a disadvantage to making lots of items with this method?

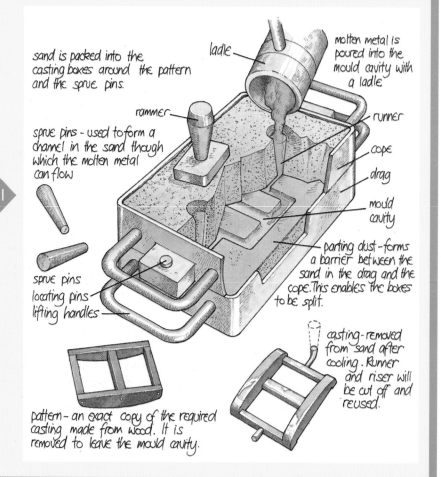

sand is packed into the casting boxes around the pattern and the sprue pins.

ladle

molten metal is poured into the mould cavity with a ladle

rammer

runner

sprue pins - used to form a channel in the sand though which the molten metal can flow

cope

drag

mould cavity

sprue pins
locating pins
lifting handles

parting dust - forms a barrier between the sand in the drag and the cope. This enables the boxes to be split.

casting - removed from sand after cooling. Runner and riser will be cut off and reused.

pattern - an exact copy of the required casting made from wood. It is removed to leave the mould cavity.

Case study – The Bulldog Buckle Co.

Special types of moulds are used in industry that can be used again and again. The Bulldog Buckle Company manufactures intricately designed belt buckles, badges and cuff links from pewter. They first model the product idea using plastic resins, carving techniques and CAD/CAM.

Green book: CAD and CAM 88

The final model is then used to make a mould to cast the pewter in. When lots of castings are needed, special multiple moulds are made to make them in one go.

Over half a million castings a week, like these, are made at The Bulldog Buckle Company

Using systems and control in manufacturing

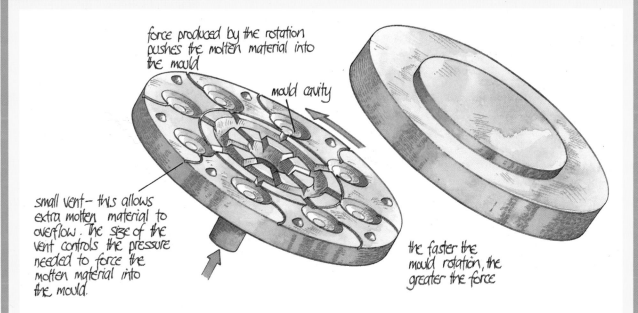

force produced by the rotation pushes the molten material into the mould

mould cavity

small vent — this allows extra molten material to overflow. The size of the vent controls the pressure needed to force the molten material into the mould.

the faster the mould rotation, the greater the force

The pressure on the liquid metal is controlled by the spinning speed of the die. Extra metal is allowed to escape to make sure that the die completely fills up

When lots of identical products are being manufactured, special control systems are often used.

■ What kinds of control systems do you use?

■ Are there some examples at home that you can think of?

■ How is quality controlled when batches of similar food items are prepared?

■ Show how you would control the quality of your finished fastener.

Using different materials

Think about the materials that are available to you. Could certain materials help you to design and make a better product? How could you use different materials to develop and make your idea?

Materials may have special properties or characteristics. You will need to choose the best material for your fastener. To do this you might like to draw up a chart to show what

your fastener needs and how different materials might meet these needs.

Fastener needs for child's harness	possible materials			
	mild steel	aluminium	brass	polyethylene polystyrene
smooth surface	✓	✓	✓	✓
hard-wearing	✓	✓	✓	✓
not easily broken	✓	✓	✓	
stiff	✓	✓	✓	✓
not brittle	✓	✓	✓	
strong	✓	✓		

Bags of ideas

Your challenge!

Many shops provide bags to carry home the products they sell. Some bags do other jobs as well, such as conserving heat or providing an extra layer of protection. Others are designed as gift wrapping. One thing all bags have in common is that they provide an ideal opportunity for the shop to advertise itself.

Your challenge is to design and make a bag that might be used by a particular shop for a specific function and/or to design the printed images that might be applied to such a bag.

Why this activity is useful

- ◆ You will develop your skills of presenting ideas for graphic products using a variety of different media and a range of techniques.

- ◆ You will need to understand the nature of the business you are designing for and the products it sells.

- ◆ You will understand how that business markets itself.

- ◆ You will learn about printing and the restrictions that might be imposed on your designing. You may have the opportunity of using computers to develop your ideas.

The broader picture . . .

Are items such as carrier bags, which are often only used once, a waste of resources? What are companies doing to make the marketing products they give away more environmentally friendly? Collect some examples to show what you have found.

Can bags be used to advertise important messages about the company or is this just a waste of time?

To be successful

You will:

★ demonstrate that you understand the way your chosen business is marketed.

★ produce a variety of ideas and make a prototype of your best idea to look as good as a manufactured article.

★ understand the printing processes involved and be able to talk confidently about how your design could be commercially produced.

★ have tried a variety of materials and processes and chosen the best ones.

★ be able to communicate your ideas to other people, such as a shopkeeper or a marketing manager.

Planning things through

▶ You should arrange to talk to someone from your chosen business about the company image and how bags are used.

▶ You should find out how other businesses use bags to market their company image and use this to help you to develop new ideas.

▶ You may need to make use of computers and will need to plan this time carefully to avoid queues and delays.

What kind of bag? What kind of image?

What sort of bag is required and what image should it have? What sort of shop are you designing for? You could make up your own shop or you could choose one that you think could do with a redesigned bag. Just imagine how much better this Challenge could be if you were designing for a real need in a real shop. You will need to undertake some research and record your findings.

Green book:
Identifying needs 90

This student had her design taken up by a major High Street store. Perhaps you could do the same!

Using a specification

If you have been able to find someone in a suitable business to help you with this work they might be able to provide you with a specification. In industry, designers are often given a specification by the customer. This is then used at several different stages of the design and production process to check that everything is being done correctly.

Green book:
Specifications 92

A specification was given to the students who redesigned the Dixons carrier bag. The company had some very clear ideas about what sort of messages they wished to communicate and what sort of people use their shops. This specification only deals with marketing. Dixons will give another specification to the company who manufacture the bags. This will be concerned only with the function of the bag (how much weight it will hold, size of handles, etc.).

An example of a performance specification for a bag

Performance specification for a bag to transport gold powder

The bag needs to stack without slipping, so a plastic material should not be used.

Will need to be powder-proof, therefore double-lined paper must be used.

Must be capable of holding 40kg.

Must carry printed information in line with COSHH regulations.

Presenting a company profile

Collect information about the company you are designing for and present this visually. You will need to find out if they have a company logo and if they use a particular palette of colours in their marketing. This may put a major restriction on what you can design.

You might begin by finding out if the company you are designing for can supply you with examples of graphics that they have used in the past.

Presenting a company profile (continued)

Perhaps you can show the sort of products they sell and the sort of people who are their customers.

Green book:
Promotional products 86 →

Here you can see how the designers have been restricted to a small range of colours. This is called a **palette**. Sometimes the designers can introduce another colour for special promotions, such as sales

Looking at existing products

When designing, it is sometimes useful to think about existing products and why they were designed in this way. Collect a sample of paper bags and carefully undo the glued seams until you have the flat **net** (engineers use the term **development** to describe a flat shape that can be folded into such a form). Discuss with a partner why you think each one was made that way. Remember: the printing is usually done before the bag is cut out and folded.

What else is special about each bag? Look carefully at the materials used. Are they all the same? Identify why different materials are used. Look carefully at any printing found on the bags. Decide how it could be done. Identify what colour palette has been used. Decide which colour would be printed first. You should record this information as a chart so that you can refer to it again at the designing stage.

Now take a second look and think about how you could make a similar product in school. What would be the stages in the manufacturing process?

Logos and trademarks

Logos and trademarks are often printed on a company's products as part of the graphic design. These are registered symbols that have been especially designed for each company and are owned by them. They are used so that other people will quickly understand who is making or selling that item.

Green book:
The images 88 →

Companies are very protective of their logos and trademarks. They often place a tiny letter or symbol, ™, alongside them for protection – a sort of 'Hands off!' message.

This means that if you are designing a bag for a business that already uses a logo you have to be very careful. You will not be able to alter any part of it without the company's permission. Also, you cannot use any part of anyone else's logo.

Logos and trademarks (continued)

Do you instantly recognise these logos and know what is likely to be on sale?

If you are using an existing logo, photocopy it to a suitable size and use it as an underlay when you develop your ideas

Using computers

If you want to make a high quality product to present to the company, you might consider using computers to help you. There are a number of alternatives that might be considered. You will need to check what is available to you.

Scanning images

Scanning images can save you lots of time, especially if you are not good at drawing!

Images saved on disk

Graphic designers save images, such as logos, electronically in computer files. They can then use them every time the customer wants a new label, bag, display or other graphic product. It is possible that the company you are designing for can supply you with logos already saved to disk.

The Stika

Although small in size, this little machine can give you some impressive results with professional-looking graphics. It can work as a scanner and cut out images that have been computer-printed or hand-drawn

Printing or plotting?

If you only have an A4 printer, this might severely restrict what you can do. A4 computer printouts can be used as colour separations. They can then be enlarged using a photocopier with different coloured ink cartridges to produce your designs.

Using computers (continued)

An A4 printer

Using a plotter cutter

An A3 plotter uses a pen to draw out your images. This usually works best if your design is a line drawing rather than solid blocks of colour. One big advantage to using a plotter is that it works on any type of paper or card.

Plain plastic carrier bags can soon be transformed to look just like a commercially printed product using vinyl cut on a plotter cutter. If you reverse your design, the vinyl makes an excellent mask for silk screen printing onto paper or fabric.

Using a computer controlled milling machine

Look how using a simple printing block has transformed this student's idea. You might experiment with machining a range of different materials

Green book:
Block printing   77

Other printing methods

There are many other ways to print your image. Find out what is available in other departments within school

Designing and Manufacturing:
Graphics in designing   105

Case study – High volume production

High volume production at Alida

If you contracted someone to print your bag design you would have to consider the volume of production. Alida Packaging would need you to order at least 250 000! Their production is highly automated and runs seven days a week. They print onto plastic sheet and make up the whole bag in one operation. By contrast, Widdup and Sons produce runs as small as 200 because they feed ready-made bags into the printing press one at a time.

A printing press at Widdup and Sons

Born again products

Your challenge!

Food manufacturers are always looking for ways of maintaining the sales of their products. You may have seen or tried a new, improved version of a familiar food product. Redeveloping food products is the way companies stay in business.

Your challenge is to identify a local or famous food and to redevelop it as a different product. First, imagine you are a member of the development team generating ideas for the new product. Then take on the role of the development chef creating the prototypes for sampling.

Why this activity is useful

◆ You will learn how companies redesign products.

◆ You can experiment and have some fun trying things out.

◆ You could try wider research methods such as using the Internet.

◆ It should extend your understanding of the function of ingredients.

The broader picture . . .

A traditional food is often redeveloped to provide a new range of products. Pizza, naan bread and Yorkshire pudding are all foods that have been redeveloped extensively. Describe the variations that you may find.

The food industry spends a lot of time trying to make a food product that you buy in the supermarket as good as a meal that you would eat in a restaurant, yet people still go out to restaurants. Why do you think this is so?

To be successful

You will:

★ Be inventive with your ideas for developing the product.

★ Experiment with ingredients to replicate the characteristics and to develop the new qualities in your product.

★ Use your understanding of food science to develop the characteristics that you need.

★ It will be obvious what the 'new' product has been developed from – everyone will recognise it!

★ People will want to buy and eat your product. You will have trialled and improved your product by testing it on potential customers.

Planning things through

▶ Identify a suitable product. Some products may be interesting but very difficult to produce in a food technology room.

▶ Use product analysis to identify the key characteristics of the product. This will help you establish the criteria for the redeveloped product.

▶ Make sure that you have time to experiment with the ideas.

▶ Organise a group of people to be your consumer panel.

Product life cycle

Companies decide when to redesign or develop a new product by looking at the product's life cycle. Find out about the stages in the life cycle of a particular product and explain this in the form of a diagram.

Manufacturers sometimes decide to give a new image to a product. Lucozade was a health drink that helped people recuperate after illness. Today it is a sports energy drink associated with athletes like Linford Christie.

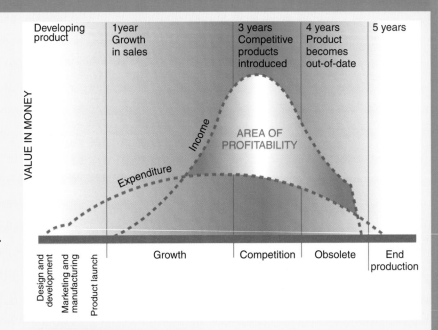

An example of a product life cycle chart

You can see how Lucozade advertising has changed in these two adverts from 1954 and 1991.

Case study – Ross Young's fish and chips

Fish and chips was one of the first restaurant meals and take-away foods. It was also one of the first frozen foods. Ross Young maintain their sales of fish and chips through continuing development and innovation.

One way that manufacturers can do this is to replicate a restaurant experience of a particular food so that consumers buy the retail product instead of going out to eat. Sale of pizzas from supermarkets is another example of a successful 'eat at home experience'.

Harry Ramsden's fish and chips are world famous and the challenge for Ross Young was to create a similar quality product. The development of this new range involved consultation with Harry Ramsden's about batter quality and processing. A new production line was installed with particular attention being given to the quality of the fryer. This required strict time and temperature controls.

Case study – the Mars ice cream

The Mars chocolate bar was launched in 1932. The Mars bar has stood the test of time and competition from an avalanche of new entrants to a highly competitive market. These days you can buy a Mars chocolate bar, a Mars milkshake drink and a Mars ice cream!

Food technology has transformed food production; in the 1980s it was not possible to make chocolate bars into ice creams. Today it is the fastest growing sector of the ice cream market.

Why is the Mars bar so successful? What other famous products can you think of that have been made into something new?

Does this give you any ideas for your own designing?

Brand image

Companies spend a lot of money developing the image of their products. They target a particular group of people (the **target audience**) and use images and words that appeal to this social and cultural group.

Companies are precise when defining their target audience.

Look at how one product is presented and describe the target audience. You will find it useful to look at:

■ TV and radio advertisements

■ magazine advertisements

■ packaging

■ colour scheme

■ logo

■ style of lettering

■ images on the packet or in adverts

■ sponsorship of sports and arts events.

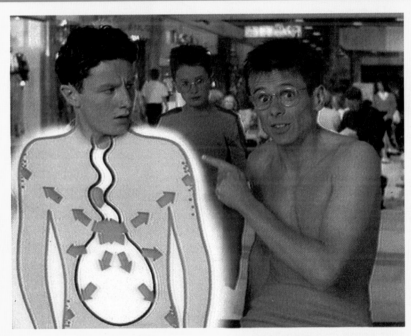

The audience for Tango is older teenage males. The Tango marketing team cultivate this image in all their publicity and their sponsorship.

Put together a mood board that reflects the image of your chosen product or develops a new image.

Ways to generate ideas

Try some of these!

Designing and Manufacturing: 102

Companies use many different techniques to generate ideas.

Some of the ideas may seem crazy at first but if they are developed you might find that they could provide the basis for an innovative product.

Key selling points

Imagine that you are describing your chosen product to someone who has never eaten it before. What makes your product so special? Quickly list the factors that come into your head. Alongside each one state how you could achieve it.

When you have finished recording your chart try to make a list of things that you might make. Carry out some research and find out if your target consumer would like them.

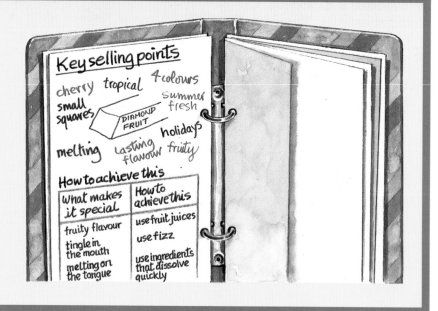

Using consumer panels

Some companies use a small group of trained people (approximately eight who are representative of their target audience) to find out their views and feelings about a product.

Set up a consumer panel in your class and ask them about your product. Use the questions opposite to start your evaluation of the product.

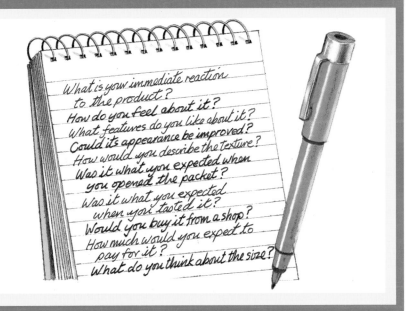

What is your immediate reaction to the product?
How do you feel about it?
What features do you like about it?
Could its appearance be improved?
How would you describe the texture?
Was it what you expected when you opened the packet?
Was it what you expected when you tasted it?
Would you buy it from a shop?
How much would you expect to pay for it?
What do you think about the size?

Customer loyalty

The marketing department of a company tries to ensure that a particular brand maintains or increases its position in the market through a never-ending process of development and innovation.

Companies spend considerable sums of money on persuading us to remain loyal to a particular brand. A long term commitment to a product may be better for profits than a short term increase in sales.

The product may have to be changed a lot over the years. Discuss with a friend or in a group ways that you think companies try to encourage our loyalty to a product. You may be able to put together a display of products and advertisements.

Get ahead!

Your challenge!

Hats can be worn for many different reasons. They can be worn to protect against hot or cold weather, for religious reasons or to make a fashion statement.

Your challenge is to design a hat that is bright, bold and unusual in shape – an individual and distinctive hat. This could be for a character in a theatrical production, someone who wants to make a statement about their beliefs or about the environment, for a celebrity who wants to be noticed, or for anyone going to a special event.

You need to decide who you are designing for and the image you want to convey. Then you can experiment with different materials and techniques to create **3D** effects.

Why this activity is useful

◆ You will have the chance to turn fantasy into reality, and a 2D design into a 3D object.

◆ Creative ideas can be modelled simply and then turned into actual products using a wide range of materials.

◆ You can experiment with a wide range of techniques including machine embroidery, sponging and dyeing fabrics, and wired appliqué.

◆ You could learn a lot about the behaviour of materials when they are being formed into objects.

The broader picture . . .

Make a collage to show functional, fashionable or religious hats.

Hats were originally made from natural fibres such as leaves, grasses and straw. They are now often made from synthetic materials. What do you feel about this change? What difference has this made?

Hats also make social statements – 'Look at me!', 'See how important I am!', or 'I'm just a humble worker'. Collect a set of pictures of hats and label each one with the message the wearer is sending.

To be successful

You will need to:

★ research a lot of traditional and modern hats

★ investigate and understand the construction of hats

★ be clear about the type of hat you want to make for your chosen person and how you will decorate it to convey the image and effect you want

★ practise different ways of joining materials.

Most important of all, remember the Challenge! Your design should be bold, bright and unusual. How might you test this when you have finished?

Planning things through

Before you begin, try to estimate how long it will take you to do each of the following:

▶ sketch out ideas in relation to your chosen user

▶ model the hat(s) using paper and other cheap materials

▶ experiment with a range of decorative techniques

▶ plan out and check the stages in constructing the hat

▶ locate all the materials you need

▶ construct and decorate your hat.

Finding out about hats

People have worn hats for hundreds of years to show who they are – their wealth, nationality, status, political beliefs, religion or occupation. Hats can be worn as a fashion statement and some hat designers are as well known as the top fashion designers.

Also hats that are traditional in other countries have become fashionable with different groups in this country. Some hats simply do a job very well – keeping you warm, sheltered from the sun or protected against injury.

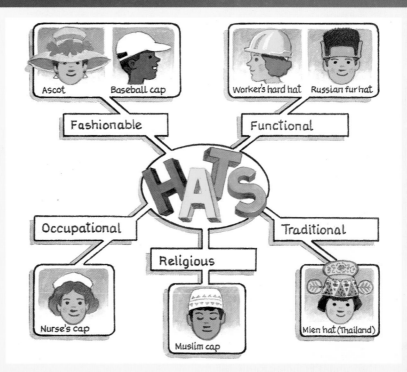

■ How many different types of hat can you think of?

■ Which of these are more about function than fashion?

■ Which would you wear? Which wouldn't you be seen dead in?!

Try brainstorming – sketch quickly as many different types of hat as you can, starting with those shown here.

Creating a mood board

Designers who work in the fashion industry often put together a **mood board** to build up a picture of their ideas. This can include magazine cuttings which set the scene that the hat would be used in and give an idea of the target group (or people you are designing for). It also includes the colour range being used and samples of materials, threads, etc.

Look at the examples of mood boards. Create one of your own to help you design the hat for your chosen person.

Looking at different hats

Where can you find out more about hats?

Magazines and catalogues have pictures of hats. Some will be formal hats for weddings. You will find other hats if you try leisure and special interest magazines such as *National Geographic*. You may be able to get information using CD-ROM. Libraries will have costume books. Your relatives and friends may have photos and postcards.

Your local museum may have some historic hats on display – these may be protective hats, fashionable hats, or part of a traditional or ethnic costume. You may be able to talk to a local milliner (hatmaker).

Collect pictures and sketches to give you ideas for your design. Note the different types of materials that are used, e.g. straw, plastic, felt. Can you suggest reasons why each of these different materials have been used?

Try to work out how the hat has been made. You may be able to take it apart or make a paper version of it.

Have a competition with your classmates to find a picture of the most unusual hat! This would make a good class display.

Modelling a hat

Collect together an assortment of lightweight fabrics like scarves and other compliant materials. Your teacher will help you to do this.

Working in pairs, create a 'hat' by winding, twisting or plaiting your materials around your friend's head. If they have long hair you can incorporate this into your hat design. You could fix it by using pins or stitching, or secure the fabric by tucking it in. Take a photo or make a quick sketch before you unravel your hat.

Measuring and making patterns

Here is one way to make the base of a hat that fits snugly to the head. Get a friend to measure round your head. This is the basic measurement you need to make any hat.

Add 15 mm seam allowance all round each segment. Join the segments together to make a cap. This can be used as a base for decoration or can have a brim, ear flaps or a peak added to it. What will happen if you change the height C–D? Experiment with paper before deciding what to do in fabric.

There are many variations that you can experiment with.

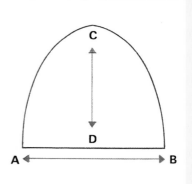

Choosing materials to construct your hat from

How soft or stiff do you want the fabric for your hat to be?

Look at the different materials that are available and test them out in a small model of your hat. Muslin is very soft and can be folded, pleated and layered, calico is much stiffer and felt is very thick. You can also use card or vilene to provide rigid sections.

Make a chart to record the different materials you try and their properties.

What special requirements will your hat have?

Decorative techniques for your hat

Try using the following techniques to decorate your hat:

- dyeing the fabrics
- appliqué
- wired appliqué
- embroidery
- any other techniques that you can find – be outrageous!

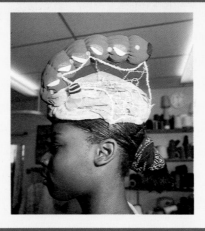

Wired appliqué

Decorative techniques for your hat (continued)

Using other materials

Think about ways to stiffen, waterproof or fasten your hat. If you want to make a base that you are going to decorate, choose a sturdy fabric like calico. Soft materials can be stiffened (**proofed**) by painting or spraying on varnish or PVA glue. These can also be coloured to decorate your hat.

Appliqué

A hat decorated with stiffened material

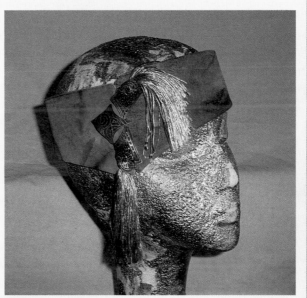

Shrinking plastic was used to decorate this hat

Modelling your finished hat

Beauchamp College students modelling their hat designs

A moving experience

Your challenge!

A stage play, a pop concert, an animated story show, or a puppet theatre all involve performances. Some rides found at theme parks can also be thought of as performances. Presentations to attract people to an event or advertise a product can use animation and other performance techniques. Many museums and theme parks have interactive displays. The best way of producing these effects is to use different types of control systems.

Your challenge is to combine mechanical, electronic, electrical and even pneumatic and hydraulic systems to produce a working model or prototype that could be used in a performance or presentation. You can choose from the ideas shown or use one of your own.

Why this activity is useful

This Challenge requires an understanding of materials, structures and systems and control. You will combine your skills in these areas with your designing and making skills.

This activity is based on teamwork and you will learn some essential teamwork skills in order to work effectively.

Producing models like this is an essential part of designing. It allows you to demonstrate your ideas without the time and expense of producing the full size design straight away.

The broader picture . . .

◆ Sophisticated technology can be used to present powerful messages and images to people, particularly young children. Can you think of some good and bad examples of this?

◆ The use of new technology has resulted in some very exciting and potentially dangerous rides at theme parks. The same technology is also used to make these rides safe. Can you find some examples of this?

◆ Some people think that the gimmicks and special effects used in the theatre are spoiling the art of acting. What do you think?

To be successful

★ You will work as a team to provide a performance with real impact. It will use as many special effects as possible, and use systems and control in interesting ways.

★ Your prototype or model must show all of the features that would be used in the final version and it should work in the same way.

★ Your prototype or model should be well presented. It will be used to test your ideas rigorously and to develop your ideas further by obtaining opinions from potential users. This information will be used to design the final version.

Planning things through

Working as a team has lots of advantages. For example, it will make it much easier to carry out the research for this project. Teamwork needs careful planning. Produce a schedule to show all of the jobs to be done, when they should be done and who will do them. You might change your schedule as you work but always be clear about deadlines.

Have regular team meetings to review progress.

Control in action

Theatres and performance

A theatre is planning a children's festival. The festival will include a series of performances and events to attract as many children as possible to the theatre.

To make the performances as dynamic as possible the theatre needs a stage design that will allow lots of special effects: flying actors, lots of movement, lighting and sound effects. The producer has visions of revolving stages, flats that can turn as well as be lifted up and down, flashing lights linked to music and sounds, trap doors in the stage to make people disappear and characters taking off and flying across the stage.

Your team has been asked to design one part of the stage for this festival. Other teams will be working on other parts.

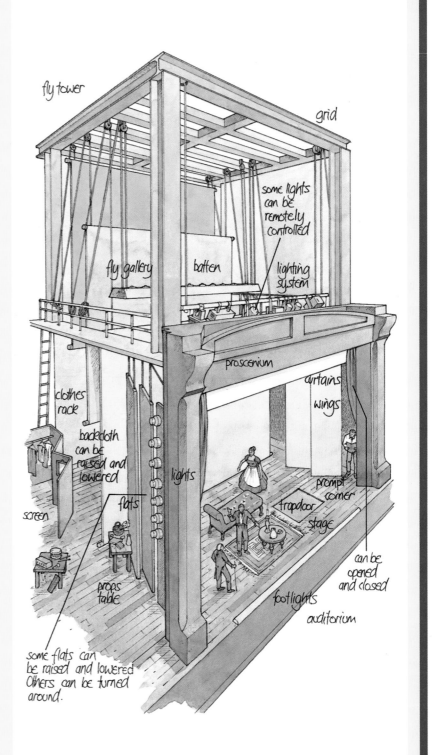

fly tower

grid

some lights can be remotely controlled

fly gallery

batten

lighting system

proscenium

curtains

wings

clothes rack

backcloth can be raised and lowered

lights

prompt corner

screen

flats

trapdoor

stage

props table

can be opened and closed

footlights

auditorium

some flats can be raised and lowered. Others can be turned around.

Control in action (continued)

Animated displays

The theatre management are very keen to make the festival appeal to as many people as possible. They would like an animated publicity display that could be taken around the schools to attract children and make them want to come to the shows.

Your team will produce a model or prototype of the display. For instance, you could make a mechanical toy that would appeal to young children.

Control in action (continued)

Music is only one part of a pop concert. The lights and special effects on stage are all part of the show.

To attract people to buy a product you often need to catch their attention. An animated display or the use of lights and special effects can help. A point-of-sale display can be used to advertise a product.

Animatronics dinosaurs were used in the film *Jurassic Park*

Animatronics

Until recently, animated films were always produced by making thousands of drawings that were then used to make the frames of the film. Many films are made using computerised models that can be combined with live action using computers. Make an animated model using control systems.

Moving sculpture

Kinetic art involves developing pieces of moving sculpture. The pieces use a range of methods for controlling movement. For example, these often use sensors and electric motors. Others use magnets and electromagnets.

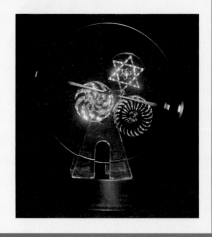

Control in action (continued)

Special effects

Many theme parks use rides where a 'car' takes you past lots of things that are happening, for example, in a ghost train. These use a range of control systems and models to create the special effects.

The same type of control systems are used in industry

Case study – Andy Roberts, Animatronics Designer

In this picture, Andy is building the mechanisms that make the doors in the roof of the clock tower open and the weather vane move

Here, Andy is working on an interactive clock tower for a Debenhams store. It chimes, has a weather vane, moving figures and doors that open and close. It also has parts that children can play with

Andy built this moving model of Nessie for the film *Loch Ness*

This is a giant pop-up book of *Sleeping Beauty* that Andy built for Disneyland Paris. It was designed by Jan Penkowski, a well known children's book writer

Getting it going

This Challenge calls upon you to combine mechanical, electronic, electrical, and even pneumatic and hydraulic systems. You will need to bring these systems together and support them with a structure. Before you start designing your system you should work through these questions to help with your planning.

All systems have an **output** that is controlled by **inputs**. The inputs have to be processed to achieve the output you require.

Output

What are you trying to achieve? What do you want to happen? Do you have the right skills and equipment available to work with electronics, mechanisms, pneumatics?

A system contains a process that produces outputs in response to inputs

This will help you to decide upon the output that you want. You can then research the output devices or actuators available to you and work out the best one to use.

Input

■ What do you want to happen?

■ How, why, when and where do you want this to happen?

■ How will you control the time each part of the performance uses?

This will help you to work out the inputs you need. You can then find out about the input devices or sensors available and decide upon the best one(s) to use.

Once you know which input and output devices you should use, you can then work out how to process the inputs to achieve the output you want.

Case study – Naser Iqbal

Naser Iqbal, a student at Dixons CTC, worked with staff at Transperience, a transport discovery park in Bradford, to develop a large bus with animated figures inside.

While researching and developing his ideas he found that control systems used in busy places with children have to be simple to maintain and almost indestructible in use. He chose the bus idea because all the control systems could be housed safely behind laminated glass.

He found it easy to think of ideas for the output of each system, but achieving this through different processes caused some headaches. The input devices were two timer switches (the sort used to turn lights off in hallways and stairs after a few seconds) and two simple rotary movements, a wheel and a crank handle.

Case study – Naser Iqbal (continued)

The control processes included using an electric motor from a sewing machine to drive a cam.

This lifted levers, using a motor from a car windscreen wiper, which allowed heads to turn in an oscillating movement. Cams were used elsewhere for making heads bob up and down, making the driver rock from side to side, and also to control the lighting through the use of microswitches.

One interesting problem involved making the starting handle more difficult to turn. During trialling it was found that the children could turn the handle so fast that the driver's head fell off! Naser increased the friction by having a spring loaded lever rubbing against a gear wheel on the main shaft. This decision had a secondary benefit as it created a realistic engine noise!

Large doors were provided on the bus so that the service engineers could easily access all the control systems to adjust and repair them.

What will you have to consider for your design? Here are some of the things Naser had to consider when designing and making.

- The size and space available.
- Safety and fire regulations.
- Power supply.
- Theme.
- Entertainment value.
- Suitability for the age group.
- Appeal and interest.
- Interactive control by the user.
- Durability.
- Access for maintenance.

Control systems

There are two main types of control system known as **open-loop** and **closed-loop control systems**.

In open-loop control systems, once the system is set or a sequence of actions set in place, it will continue without taking any account of what is happening to the output.

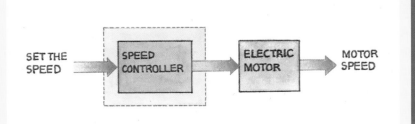

Open-loop control of the speed of an electric motor. If the motor is loaded its speed will decrease. With open-loop control no steps are taken to correct this

Control systems (continued)

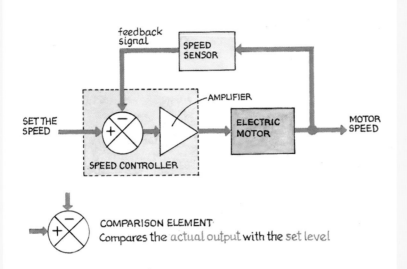

Closed-loop control of the speed of an electric motor. If the motor is loaded its speed will decrease. This information is fed back to the controller which adjusts the speed of the motor accordingly

Closed-loop control systems make use of **feedback**. Information is fed back from the output to a controller to adjust the system.

The simplest type of closed-loop, or feedback, control is an ON/OFF system. The feedback signal is used to turn the system on and off depending on what is happening at the output. Electronics systems kits contain a board called a **comparator**. This can be used as the comparison element in an ON/OFF control system.

The example below makes use of block diagrams. This is a very useful way of representing a system.

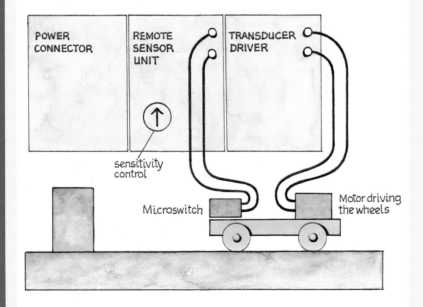

ON/OFF control of an electric motor. You could try replacing the microswitch with a light sensor or a magnetic switch and magnet. You can use a comparator with the light sensor to set the light level to control the vehicle

Systems and sub-systems

When you are analysing a system, it is often sensible to break it down into a series of smaller sub-systems. For each sub-system you should:

- draw a block diagram

- decide which input and output devices you could use

- work out how to process the inputs to achieve the outputs you want

- work out how to connect the sub-systems together.

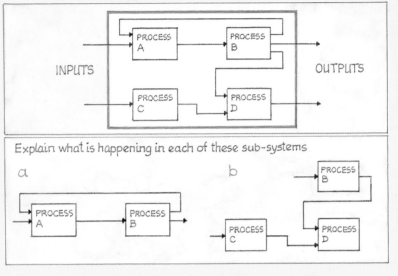

Systems and sub-systems

Choosing your inputs and outputs

You can use a table like this to help you choose the equipment you need. This one has been partly completed by a student.

When you have done this you can also work out if it would help to use a computer in your system.

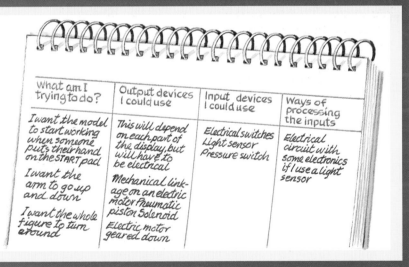

What am I trying to do?	Output devices I could use	Input devices I could use	Ways of processing the inputs
I want the model to start working when someone puts their hand on the START pad	This will depend on each part of the display, but will have to be electrical	Electrical switches Light sensor Pressure switch	Electrical circuit with some electronics if I use a light sensor
I want the arm to go up and down	Mechanical linkage on an electric motor Pneumatic piston Solenoid		
I want the whole figure to turn around	Electric motor geared down		

Will it be all right on the night?

If you are using electronic or mechanical systems together you will need a structure to support parts and components.

Think about these questions:

- What will the structure need to support?

- What could you use to make it?

- Will it let you modify your ideas quickly and easily?

- Will it blend with the surroundings?

Stylish sets

Your challenge!

In the early 1980s, Ettore Sottsass, the famous Italian designer, and his contemporaries established a design style known as 'Memphis'. They decided to follow just one rule in their designing – the outcome must be fun!

Imagine what a great job it must be designing products that are fun. You are going to use the work of modern designers like Ettore Sottsass to help you to create some fun products.

Your challenge is to design an unusual gift for a friend or relative. Your gift should make them smile whilst serving a useful purpose. The gift should be a group of items such as a mirror and two candlesticks, or a brush, comb and hand-held mirror.

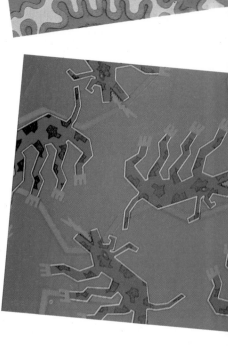

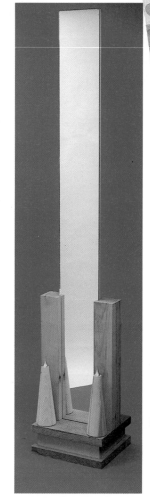

Why this activity is useful

◆ This challenge will enable you to investigate the work of exciting modern designers and use their ideas as a source of inspiration.

◆ You will be able to use your research skills to find and select materials to make a mood board to inspire your design activity.

◆ You will look at the importance of form and function when designing.

◆ You will make it easier for yourself by working out how to manufacture a matching set with the minimum amount of extra work for each piece.

The broader picture . . .

◆ Why do you think it is important that some designers, architects and artists produce outrageous ideas?

◆ It is unusual to find people in this country who enjoy modern art and design. Why do most of us surround ourselves with more traditional products?

◆ Think about an ordinary, everyday product and how you would redesign it so that it is extraordinary.

◆ Conduct a survey to find out what other people think about modern designs. Perhaps you could ask their opinion on your product redesigns.

To be successful

You will:

★ show how your work reflects the influence of modern designers. Annotate your design ideas to show this

★ create ideas for the set of products that work well together. Pay careful attention to surface pattern, colour and texture

★ plan your production of the set and use techniques to make production quicker than if you were making each piece separately.

People viewing your set of products should stand back in amazement. It's much more fun if it takes them a while to work out what the items are.

Planning things through

▶ Work on creating your set of gifts and choosing your surface decoration at the same time.

▶ As your products may be quite different from anyone else's, you will have to plan your making very thoroughly.

▶ Produce a plan for making your set. Think about how to make production quicker and easier for yourself – where can you save time?

Post Modernist style – visual sources

Flash by Dorothy Hafner

Tea and coffee pots by Aldo Rossi

Fridge-freezer from the Wizards
Collection by Roberto Pezzetta

Antelope Table by Matthew Hilton

Finding out about modern design

Designers are always looking for something new but it is important that they create products that people want. Things that at first appear weird or unusual soon become commonplace and this is the way that designers encourage change. These two high-tech designs illustrate how designers have set out to change ideas.

■ What makes the Lloyds building different from other buildings in London?

■ What kind of people might buy a modern chair like the one shown in the picture?

The Lloyds building in London

Armchair, *Zyklus*, by Peter Maly

■ Design a suite of matching furniture to go with the chair.

■ What are the main features of high-tech designs?

Case study – Changing our expectations

Modern chair by Nathalie du Pasquier

The chair shown here challenges our expectations of what a chair should look like. Many people find designs like this difficult to accept because they are so different from anything that they have seen before. You cannot fail to notice them!

The *Dual Cyclone DC01* is currently Britain's best-selling upright vacuum cleaner

When James Dyson created the *Dual Cyclone DC01* upright vacuum cleaner he not only challenged the way that traditional vacuum cleaners work but also their appearance. This innovative product has proved to be very successful.

A 19th century zoetrope, or magic lantern

It is not just modern designers who set out to surprise us!

Generating ideas for a set of products

Collect examples of modern designs that you like. They could come from books or magazines or you might like to take some photographs of your own. Use these examples to create a mood board that will inspire you when you are designing.

Creating a mood board
Fantasy Headwear Challenge 42

You will need to explore a range of design ideas before selecting one. It is important to maintain a questioning but open-minded approach when developing your ideas.

- When will the set of products be used?
- What will they be used for?
- Who will they be used by?

- What materials and equipment do I have?
- What do I want the set to look like?
- How am I going to make them look extraordinary?
- What are going to be the common features across the set of products?
- How am I going to ensure that they are really good quality products?

Designing and manufacturing a set of products

A set of products will have some common features. When you are designing them you need to think about how they are going to be made. You should be able to produce a plan of how to make the set so that it is quicker and easier than if you were designing and making each piece separately. They should all match and be of good quality.

Think about the following questions:

- Can you reduce the number of parts and different materials used?

This student designs for manufacture, saving time and making it easier to make a set

This student designs and makes the set as individual pieces. It is much harder work and takes longer

Designing and manufacturing a set of products (continued)

■ Can you save time by making more of your parts the same size?

■ Could they be prepared together, rather than one at a time?

■ Could any parts of your design be moulded?

■ Could you use standard templates?

■ Could you work as a group and divide up the work?

■ Could you use a jig to make the parts more quickly and accurately?

■ Could you use CAD to enlarge or reduce the scale of a pattern or design to put on each item?

Interesting surface treatment

Looking back at the examples of modern designs shown in this Challenge, you will notice that many of the products have interesting surface treatment. Examples include:

■ colour

■ pattern

■ texture

■ natural finishes

■ combinations of materials.

See if you can find examples of modern products that show these qualities.

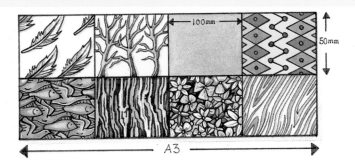

Draw eight rectangular boxes 100 × 50 mm. Find as many interesting ways as you can to fill the boxes. Be prepared to experiment and have some fun.

Your ideas can be as crazy as you like! If you do not experiment you will not create anything new

You might eventually choose to use one of your ideas to decorate your product.

Application of surface decoration

The example in the first picture shows a small mirror that a student designed as a part of a manufacturing exercise.

Surface decoration can change the nature of a product. In these three examples, the mirror frame becomes much more fun.

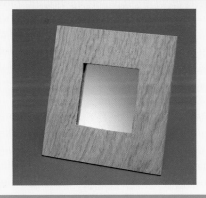

Temporary furniture

Your challenge!

Have you ever thought how much space is taken up by items such as furniture? Do you really need such large and permanent structures? There are lots of situations where you might use temporary structures – on the beach, by the riverside, in a tent or caravan, in your own garden or to assist someone after a major disaster.

Your challenge is to identify a need and then design and make a useful structure to fulfil that need. It will fold up or can be taken apart so that it will take up a lot less space. This will make it easier to transport or store. It might be for use indoors or outside, so you will need to think very carefully about suitable materials.

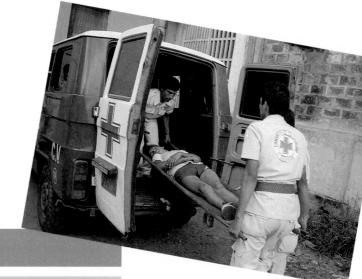

Why this activity is useful

◆ You will be able to design and make something that is really useful to someone.

◆ You will be able to further develop your understanding of structures and the properties of materials by experimentation.

◆ Your investigation might involve talking or writing to experts.

◆ You will be working to high levels of accuracy and will need to measure and shape materials precisely.

The broader picture . . .

◆ Do we use too much material when we design and make items for our homes? Find out how homes are furnished in other countries. You might discover some very clever ways of reducing the amount of materials used.

◆ Many people in the world lead nomadic lives. Find out what this means and see if you can discover the way they solve their furnishing needs.

◆ Where might collapsible furniture meet a practical human need? Think about what structures would be useful.

To be successful

You will:

★ identify a need and carry out a thorough investigation.

★ develop a specification for your product and will use this to evaluate your ideas.

★ evaluate your product or existing products using comparative testing.

★ draw and model a variety of ideas, and then make your best idea at full size or to scale. It should work as well as a commercially manufactured product.

Planning things through

▶ Think carefully about the need you are designing for. It might be better if you are making something for someone else rather than yourself.

▶ Make a list or a chart of the things you will have to consider or will have to find out about.

▶ You will have to work accurately and might need to make several identical pieces. Think about ways to do this.

▶ Be realistic about what you can achieve in the time available. Check with your teacher if there are any other restrictions.

Product evaluation – wheelchairs

Wheelchairs are an excellent example of a collapsible structure. The main parts fold together and many other parts are foldable or removable.

Our bottoms are not well designed for sitting despite them being well padded! Some quite hard chairs are just as comfortable as soft chairs. This is because we support ourselves on two points of our pelvis. If we sit on a seat that is just made of fabric it can be very uncomfortable. This can be a big problem for wheelchair users. Can you think of ways to adapt a wheelchair so that it is comfortable to sit in but it is still easy to fold up? Draw your ideas for a new, improved wheelchair and discuss this with your classmates. Make a simple model from card of how this would work.

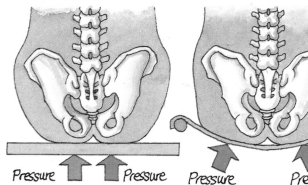

Pressure Pressure

HARD SEAT
Support taken on bone

Pressure Pressure

SLUNG SEAT
Causes pressure on buttocks

Case study – Royal College of Art students' work

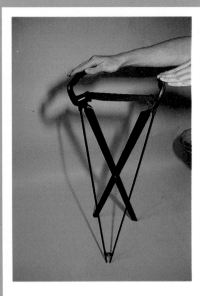

This prototype (left), by Kim Field, is a shooting stick that unfolds into a seat. It is lightweight and portable so can be used for outdoor activities like fishing, or for watching sports events such as horse racing

Volker Hellwig designed this dual purpose folding structure. It is a chair that can also be turned into a table

Understanding frame structures

Structures are made to support a load. Loads that do not move around are known as **static loads**. A stack of plates on a kitchen shelf is an example of a static load. But many structures have to cope with moving loads; these are known as **dynamic loads**. Every time you sit on a chair or lean it at an angle you are exerting a dynamic load. Dynamic loads produce much greater forces than static loads. It is usually a dynamic load that causes a structure to collapse.

Frame structures are made up of separate parts called **members** or **beams**. This is easy to understand when you can see all of the separate members, but sometimes these are hidden behind panels.

Red book:
Identifying structures 68

It is easy to see the separate members used in this frame structure

Forces

There are five main types of force that can be applied to a structure. You will need to consider these when testing your models.

COMPRESSION FORCES are PUSHING forces...

TENSION FORCES are PULLING forces...

BENDING FORCES simply BEND structures... ..or do they?

TORSION FORCES are TWISTING forces...

SHEARING FORCES are CUTTING forces

Devising your own tests

You will need to devise your own tests to see how these forces affect your structures. You can work in a group.

Make sure that your tests are fair. Each model will need to be tested in the same way if you are going to be able to make comparisons.

Measure how much material has been used and how much movement occurs when a force is applied to each structure.

What other things will you have to think about to make sure that your tests are fair?

Beams, members and sections

Your structure may be built from separate members. One way to do this is to make it from big, strong pieces. However, if your design is to be lightweight then you will need to make sure that it is built from the lightest, strongest shaped pieces that you can find.

Carry out some tests on the material sections. The term **section** refers to the shape of the end of the material. If an object is cut in two we refer to the view of the shape made by the cut as a **cross-section**.

Here are some typical sections that materials come in. You will need to conduct some fair tests to decide which are the strongest

The information gained from this might allow you to design a very strong structure that is light in weight or interesting to look at.

Try building some new sections of your own. Work as a group and share the results. Strips of thin material off-cuts such as MDF or plywood can be glued together with PVA adhesive to create U, H, T and I sections. Can you see why these sections are described by using letters of the alphabet? Can you create others based on letters?

Sheet metal such as aluminium can be folded to create lots of other variations.

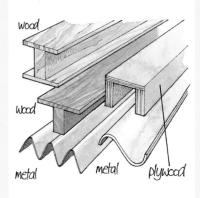

wood

wood

metal   metal   plywood

Red book:
Testing   62

Fabrics are particularly suitable for withstanding tension forces in a structure. Can you think of others that might be used in this way? Can you undertake some tests to see whether such materials would stretch too much?

You will need to think about how you can measure the amount of pull. You will need to make your tests fair. How can you do this when testing different materials?

Green book:
Thinking about materials   105

Stabilising structures

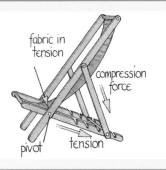

fabric in tension

compression force

pivot   tension

Although your Challenge is to make a collapsible structure it will need to be stable when carrying a load. **Triangulation** provides one of the easiest ways to stabilise structures.

Many folding structures, such as deck chairs, are based around triangulation.

Red book:
A child's chair   69

Stabilising structures (continued)

Look very carefully at a range of folding structures.

Identify how triangulation stabilises the structure. Can you base your ideas upon an existing structure?

Consider ways in which a stabilising member actually locks the structure. Draw as many alternative ways as you can. Compare your drawings with those of your classmates. Are there things that are common to all of the examples you have found? Add notes to your drawings to explain the similarities and differences. You could produce a chart to compare them.

Identifying needs

What sort of structure is required and what job will it have to do? You should try to design to fulfil a real need for someone.

Brainstorming in a group might be a good starting point

Red book:
Brainstorming   91

Prototype or model?

Depending upon the size of the structure you have identified and the restrictions you have (time, materials or facilities), you will have to decide whether you are going to make a full size prototype or a scale model. In either case, you will need to work with a high degree of accuracy.

Green book:
Modelling   42

You can still do a full evaluation of your product in model form. You may not be able to see if a chair is comfortable to sit on but you

These two examples are accurately made models. Can you tell which one is full size and which is a scale model? The one on the left is a roughly made lash-up

can test whether it is a strong enough structure to withstand the loads that it will have to carry. You can also check to see if a model is capable of collapsing as required. Can you devise some ways in which you could test accurate scale-model chairs?

Red book:
Testing   62

Making accurate models

Look at this example of a simple folding mechanism. This is commonly found on products such as clothes dryers. It looks extremely easy to make, doesn't it? However, it requires a very high degree of accuracy. If you do not get the measurement between the pivot points exactly the same it will not fold up.

Imagine you wanted to cut and drill lots of these as part of your collapsible structure. You might set about making a jig to ensure that each piece is identical.

Manufacturers make jigs, use special tools and computer controlled machinery to ensure consistent quality, regardless of the skill of the person doing the job.

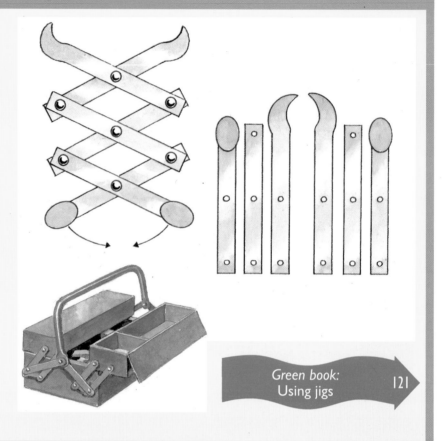

Green book:
Using jigs
121

Flexible and temporary joints

There are many ways in which you can produce flexible joints suitable for a collapsible structure. Consider some of these methods in your design ideas and then discuss them with your teacher.

pronged nut

metal or plastic nuts

washer

using frame connectors

pop rivets

rivets

screw cup

short pin used to stop rail turning over

Using CAD/CAM in this Challenge

If you make a scale model there is the potential for using CAD/CAM. For example, you could use a CNC milling machine to accurately cut out parts for a model of a chair from rigid polystyrene sheet. This would enable you to look at some of the issues that manufacturers have to consider.

Making sure that you get the maximum amount of pieces from a sheet of material can be difficult. Using CAD makes this task easier as it is simple to move pieces around on the screen. Fitting as many pieces onto a sheet to make maximum use of the material and reduce wastage is known as **nesting**.

Using CAD also makes the job of repeating shapes easier and more accurate than using other methods such as templates and patterns.

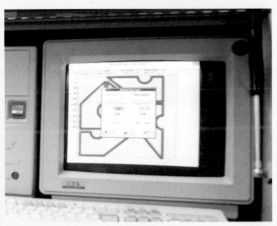

Green book:
Nesting   62

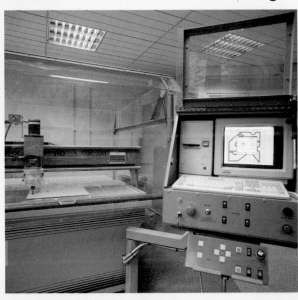

Look at how little waste material there is. This is an example of nesting achieved by using CAD/CAM

Testing and evaluating models

If you want to test whether a scale model of a structure will take the necessary load, the materials and fastenings you use will have to be the same as a full-size product and to the same scale.

Sometimes, making models is the only way of testing whether structures will perform the job they are required to do. It would be impractical to build a bridge, for example, load it with trucks and then wait for a storm to see whether it collapses. Engineers now use sophisticated computer software so that they can undertake this sort of testing without having to construct a model from rigid materials.

The final evaluation will need to take into account the testing you have done. You should also think about the original need that you identified and decide whether your final proposal would be suitable for the people it was designed for. You will need to decide whether your design meets all of the criteria in your specification.

Green book:
Evaluation   115

Feeding special groups

Your challenge!

Nowadays people demand choice whether they are eating a meal on an aircraft, in a restaurant or in a motorway service station. Meals or dishes have to be made to suit a variety of tastes and sometimes different dietary needs. Many companies buy ready prepared meals from a supplier. These can be kept frozen or chilled before being served to their customers.

A company wants to buy a new meal that can be offered to customers with special dietary needs. **Your challenge**, as the manufacturer and supplier, is to identify a specific dietary need and then design and make a prototype of a suitable dish. Your findings and new idea may then be presented to the company.

Why this activity is useful

In developing a product for individuals or groups with particular dietary needs you will have to carry out research to identify the group that you will design for. You will also learn about the sources and functions of the main nutrients.

The dish will be eaten by many people so you must think about hygiene regulations and consider the keeping qualities of the product.

The broader picture . . .

The range and variety of non-meat meals in restaurants has grown recently. Can you explain why?

Fast food outlets are popular with teenagers and young adults. Can you suggest ways in which the menu can provide healthy eating alternatives or meet special dietary needs?

Chefs such as Anton Mosiman have shown that healthy eating and gastronomic pleasure are compatible. Can you suggest how caterers can make their meals meet healthy eating guidelines?

To be successful

You will:

★ identify through research a group with a particular dietary need

★ use a database to analyse the nutritional content of your ideas

★ develop an idea for an appetising product by experimenting, modelling and testing a range of ideas

★ understand how to create interesting food products when your choice of ingredients is restricted

★ advise on how the product is to be stored until use

★ consider how it will be produced in high volume.

Planning things through

▶ Plan your research well and identify a group that has a particular dietary need.

▶ Your teacher will help you analyse the nutrient content of your product. Allow time for this.

▶ Think up a variety of ways to help you to test your ideas.

▶ Don't forget to allow time to put together your presentation.

What's so special about dietary needs?

Does everybody eat the same kind of food? Do any of your family or friends prefer to, or have to, eat special diets? People choose to eat vegetarian or vegan diets for a variety of reasons such as religious, ethical or ecological beliefs against eating meat. There are even different sorts of vegetarian diets. Find out if anyone in your class eats a special diet.

Here are some other types of special diets:

- ■ low cholesterol
- ■ low calorie
- ■ no lactose
- ■ low salt
- ■ Halal
- ■ Kosher
- ■ high fibre.

Find out as much information as you can about the needs of the people who have particular dietary requirements.

What foods can we buy for people with special diets? Many food manufacturers produce specialist dishes or meals. Find out about the range of dishes available and record your findings as a chart.

Dishes for special diets			
Name of dish	Special dietary need	Manufacturer's name	Why it is suitable
mushroom quiche	vegetarian	Finsbury's	Uses vegetarian cheddar cheese, animal products, no flesh
baked beans	vegetarian high fibre	Helga	No animal products 3.7g fibre per 100g.

Using your research

How might the manufacturer have decided which special groups to design for? For which special diet was the widest range of dishes available?

Product designers use existing products as jumping off points to help them generate ideas. Did your research give you any ideas for a new product or ideas for improving one that already exists?

Who are you designing for?

You may want to focus on a specific area such as vegetarian meals. Or you may take a more general approach and look at reduced fat meals. You may find out a lot of information about people's general eating habits and use it to identify a need.

You should research the type of specialist dishes people need rather than just thinking up a new product. This should also tell you if there is a need for something completely new or if an existing product can be improved.

Make sure that your own market research is appropriate for the group you are researching and for your aims.

Remember: each question should help you find out information you can use in your designing.

Checklist

Aim to research fat reduced meals for the general population

My research will be designed to find out general information

Ask a wide range of people: the group will include a range of needs

Include males and females

Include a range of age groups

Aim to research vegetarian meals for teenagers

Find out about a specialist diet

Ask a select group (eg teenagers): The group all have the same specialist need. (eg vegetarian.)

Include a cross-section for this group (there may be more teenage girls chosen)

Choose age range appropriate to the group (eg teenagers)

Using the results to help your design

Record the findings from your research as bar charts or tally charts. Explain what the findings have told you (**analysis**) and which group of people you have identified as your focus group. Clearly record any decisions you make about your design ideas for a specialist meal for this group.

What needs to be considered?

Collect as much information as possible about the specialist diet you have identified. Find out as much as you can about the group's dietary needs to help you decide which ingredients to include and which to leave out.

You may find it useful to record your findings in the following format.

Specialist diet	Western vegetarian	Gluten-free diet
Other names for same diet	Ovo-lacto vegetarian	Gluten restricted, wheat-free, coeliac disease
Characteristics	No meat or meat products of any type. No fish, fowl or products with lard or gelatine. Dairy products & eggs permitted. Cheese made with non-animal rennet	No foods prepared with wheat, rye, barley, oats
Guidelines and additional info	Some vegies do not drink caffeine & avoid other foods	Products with starch made from arrowroot, corn, potato, rice starch, soya allowed. Gluten-free bread mix allowed. Cereals strictly forbidden. Milk & milk products not allowed. Care with fats & dressings made with milk.

Changes for the best?

The menu opposite shows a selection of dishes from The Charnley Arms. Some changes have been written at the side of the menu to show how it is suitable for different dietary needs. See if you are able to make more suggestions.

skin has been removed, so less fat – healthy eating

GREENALLS
CHARNLEY ARMS

CHARNLEY SPECIALITIES

MINTED LAMB CASSEROLE
Succulent tender diced leg of lamb in a rich mint gravy.

CAJUN CHICKEN
A tender chicken breast seasoned with Cajun spices.

VEGETARIAN DISHES

VEGETABLE TIKKA MASALA
A rich Tikka Masala sauce with carrots, peas, green beans and sweetcorn.

PASTA FLORENTINE
A delicious combination of farfalle pasta, with red and yellow pepper strips, leaf spinach and vegetarian Cheddar cheese with a delicate touch of spice.

SALADS & PLATTERS

CHARNLEY CHICKEN SALAD
Tender slices of chicken breast served with a selection of crisp salads and vegetables and topped with mozzarella cheese.

FISH DISHES

POACHED SALMON
A delicious salmon fillet topped with lemon parsley butter.

All our hot platters are served with a choice of potatoes, vegetables or salad.

not fried, suitable for low fat diet

good source of fibre – healthy eating

strict vegetarian or western vegetarian (no meat or meat products)

Case study – special meals in flight

David Letherman (Support Services Manager) of LSG/Sky Chefs says:

'There is an increasing trend for passengers travelling by air to request meals other than the standard provided by the airline, whether for dietary or religious reasons. It is now considered unusual for a flight to leave without any special meals on board. The most common type of special meal is vegetarian, and all airlines have a standard vegetarian meal as an alternative to the usual meal offered.

'The caterer must include everything, not just the hot main course. A vegan will not be happy given butter for his bread and milk for his coffee, however much he enjoyed a beansprout salad and nut roast with tomato sauce.

'LSG/Sky Chefs produce a wide range of special meals. One we cannot produce is a Kosher meal because of all the special requirements. Special airline Kaddasia meals are bought in that will cover all passengers' requirements. These are frozen and used as required.

'Each airline has its own menus and special meals which we produce. There is a specification and photograph produced so chefs know the exact content and what each should look like.

Class: Economy
Menu: Hindu/Muslim
Description: Dinner
             entrée

Your teacher has the recipes for these dishes

LSG **Lufthansa Service SKY Chefs**

Class: Economy
Menu: All Hindu/
             Muslim/Indian
             meals
Description: Dinner tray set-up

'Each meal must not only look the same but be the same size and weight. The airline is paying for the meals and they have a set budget within which they must work. If portions are too large they may not look attractive, there will be wastage and Sky Chefs will lose money. If the portions are too small, the airline may get passenger complaints as we have not done what we have been paid for.

'Meals are made up on a production line and must all look exactly the same. Usually special meals are made to order, and these too must look just like the airline specification. A team of workers puts the meals together but trials are being held in America to see if a robot can carry out this task.'

Is your meal suitable for your chosen special diet?

This is part of a report by a student who has designed a meal that is low in fat. It was written after the first trial of the prototype cheese sauce that has been included in the meal.

The meal I made was quite successful. It was colourful and looked attractive. To make sure the sauce was low in fat I used semi-skimmed milk, light margarine and a low fat cheddar cheese. The texture was creamy but not as rich as usual. I could maybe make it richer by adding low fat fromage frais next time. To improve the appearance I will use a different cheese as the cheddar was light-coloured and the sauce looked un-interesting; a more yellow cheese would be better. The fat content was lower than usual (see nutritional database). I could make it even lower by using skimmed milk.

By tasting and testing the prototype it is possible to see what is working and what is not. From this trial you can make changes to the recipe to make it look or taste better or to change the nutritional value. Make sure you record clearly how you have made your meal suitable for the specialist diet and any changes you have to make.

One way of modelling your ideas and checking the nutritional content is to use a database. You can do this before and after the recipe is made so you can see the differences.

You will need to ask your target group what they think of the meal by using taste panels.

Red book:
Modelling food ideas 104

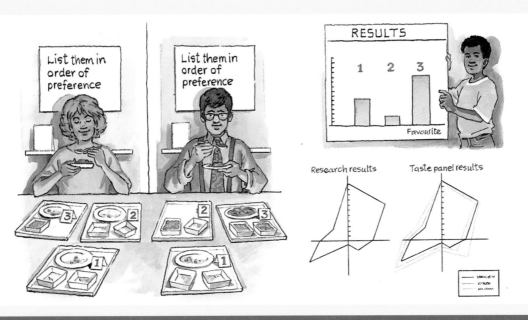

Planning production

Each stage of the food production system must be planned and monitored, from the input of the raw materials to the output of the final product.

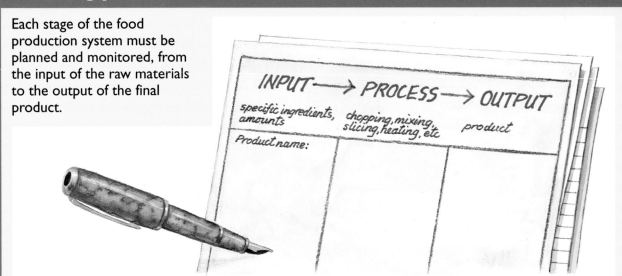

Try drawing a simple flow diagram of the product you have made, recording the stages that you go through to make it. Use the chart above to show input, processes and output.

Use the flow chart below as an example. It shows the stages involved in making a cheese sauce. Decide which food has all the others added to it and put this on the left hand side of the page, put all the other ingredients in order across the top.

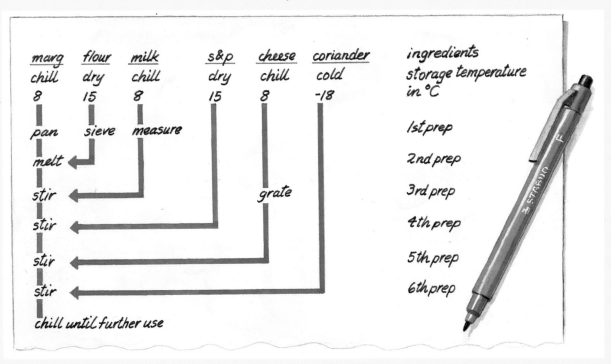

Temperature control

Indicate in different colours on your flow chart where the temperature should be checked or controlled to ensure that micro-organisms do not multiply rapidly. How could this be done?

In the food industry they will identify the safety points and the quality points. A **safety point** is any point where there may be a danger to the consumer, for example food poisoning if it is kept at the wrong temperature. A **quality point** is one that makes sure that all the products come out the same and are always of good quality.

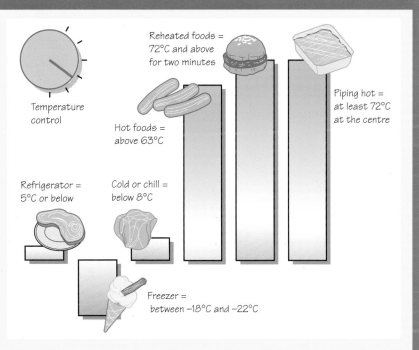

Temperature control

Reheated foods = 72°C and above for two minutes

Hot foods = above 63°C

Piping hot = at least 72°C at the centre

Refrigerator = 5°C or below

Cold or chill = below 8°C

Freezer = between −18°C and −22°C

Quality assurance

To ensure that products are all the same size and to help speed up production, companies use frames, templates and moulds.

They also use automatic weighing devices to ensure portion control, and metal detection systems.

Green book:
Control system   31

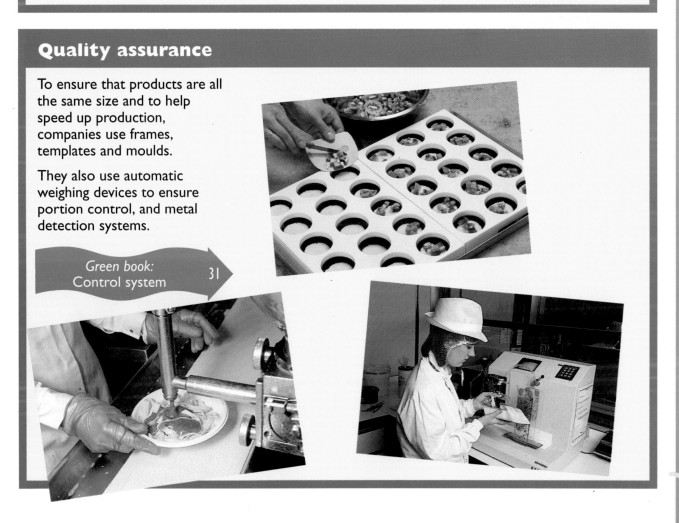

Outdoor pursuits

Your challenge!

It is vital to be warm, dry and safe, as well as comfortable, when taking part in activities such as climbing, skiing, mountain biking and walking. The invention of new fabrics has revolutionised these sports with lightweight, high performance clothing and equipment.

Your challenge is to design a textile item to be used by school students when taking part in one kind of outdoor pursuit. You will make a prototype and provide a design portfolio to communicate your ideas.

Why this activity is useful

- There are lots of interesting outdoor pursuits equipment and garments for you to learn about.

- It is demanding to design for clients with specialist needs.

- You will investigate new developments in textiles and how they have made a real difference in outdoor pursuits and sports.

- You will find out more about the properties and structure of textiles.

- You will learn about designing items to be produced in high volume and improve your construction skills in making the item.

The broader picture . . .

◆ Sometimes new materials are developed at high cost, for example for space travel, that later have commercial uses. Is the cost of space exploration justifiable in this context?

◆ New materials enable people to do dangerous things more safely. Is this always a good idea?

◆ What other 'costs' might new materials have?

◆ In the early part of this century, society required that women wore long and heavy clothing for sports such as tennis. This often limited their performance. Describe the changes that have taken place over time in the clothing used in one sport.

To be successful

★ You will design and make a high quality prototype.

★ It will be designed and made to meet the needs of outdoor pursuits students.

★ You will have a thorough, well presented record of your research, plans, ideas and actions.

★ You will produce a plan for high volume production, including the type of fabrics to be used and the best method of production.

Planning things through

You will be working independently in this Challenge.

You will need to:

▶ Research the type of activity, existing equipment and performance requirements, especially for safety.

▶ Find out about the personal needs of the students taking part, such as their spending money, sizes, preferences.

▶ Evaluate your item in action (as safely as possible!).

Finding out about existing outdoor pursuits products

Design attributes for
Skiwear

Waterproof
Warm
Lightweight
Enable you to stretch
and bend
Bright colour so you will
be seen

There are a number of ways that you can find out more about these products. For example, you could:

■ Make a class display of outdoor pursuits products and collect information about them.

■ Organise a comparison of different brands of the same product.

Record as much information as possible in a graphical way, such as a chart or poster.

List the design attributes that you would expect from the product.

Red book:
Evaluating other products 120

South Pole Tent Specifications

Aircraft-grade Aluminium Poles
The highest grade Easton 7075-T9 aluminium alloy is used for a combination of light-weight, flexibility and strength.

Computer-aided Catenary Cut Design
SPT use computer precision to cut the tent cloth in an exact arc and create a three-dimensional shape that is as light as a drum.

Internal Guying Points
All expedition tents have internal guylines that resist wind deformation, giving increased stability.

Full-coverage Fly Sheet
Each tent comes with a breathable flysheet that allows water vapour to escape, preventing condensation.

Supercoated floors
Tent floors have 5 coatings of polyurethane to create a finish that is waterproof to 165psi.

Here is an example of some of the design attributes of a tent made for extreme conditions where failure could be life threatening

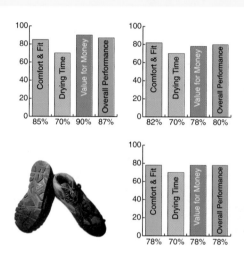

Here is an example of a comparative test that has been carried out on boots

Case study – Aquablade by Speedo

You may have seen swimmers at the 1996 Olympics wearing a revolutionary new swimming costume designed and manufactured by Speedo.

Aquablade has 8% lower surface resistance than Speedo's swimsuit for the last Olympics, and 23% less than a conventional Nylon Lycra swimwear fabric

The suit has a stripe pattern created by the addition of a water repellent resin. The rough and smooth stripes produce two currents, one slow and one fast. This creates a vertical vortex, or spiral of water, which increases the water flow, keeping it closer to the body. As a result the swimmer cuts through the water as if on rails!

The demands of skiing

To design and make skiwear for competition events, manufacturers must be up-to-date with both technological innovations and the changing requirements of the sports themselves. There are different requirements for skiing downhill, for slalom and for jumping events.

While a downhill one-piece suit cannot contribute much to the victory of its wearer as the skis or skiing skills, it can be the determining factor if the difference between winning and losing is a matter of $\frac{1}{100}$ th of a second.

Functions of a good downhill suit	How this is achieved
Must have a smooth surface for low air resistance	High gauge tricot cloth made of very fine yarns of nylon or polyester interknitted with polyurethane yarns. Calendered for smoother surface
Flexible to respond to body movement Resistant to surface creasing and flapping Expands and contracts quickly and smoothly	Double-layer fabric that is composed of cloth similar to surface cloth plus a circularly knitted cloth
Fits the body best in a crouching position	Considerable planning in terms of the cutting, direction of sewing, method of sewing, position of fasteners
Fulfils International Ski Federation requirements	Ban on plastic coating or film lamination Airflow should be 30 litre/m²/sec or above Must be made of single cloth material

Finding out about new fabrics

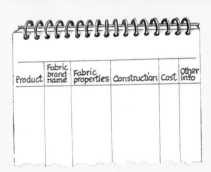

Find out more about how new fabrics are used in outdoor pursuits products. Use your class collection as a starting point.

Record your information on a chart like the one shown.

What do they mean?

As you will have already realised, there is a great deal of jargon used to describe outdoor pursuits products. What do you think these examples mean?

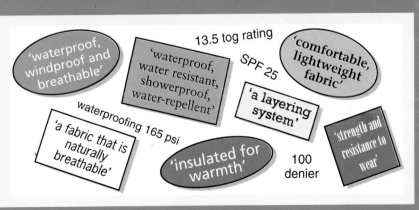

How will you choose the right materials and processes?

A manufacturer specifies the materials it will use very carefully after testing a number of suitable ones.

You will need to carry out careful research to choose fabric with the right properties and that is the best suited to being manufactured in high volume.

What tests can you carry out to make sure that you choose the right materials and processes?

Design for a new rucksack/Materials and manufacturing considerations

Bag - main body - durability, bound seams that will not pull apart, fits body comfortably, water resistant
Base - double thickness of material for durability, strong seams
Straps - strength, padding for comfort, adjustability, withstand constant tugging and tension
Drawstring - withstand constant pulling, tension and wear
Other components - buckles and fasteners

Reaction to substances

Waterproofing and water resistance

Tear strength

Testing durability of components

Performance finishes

Different finishes are applied also to enhance the properties of a fabric. Find out how these might be useful for your product.

brushing

anti-static

mothproofing

flame resistant

stiffening

shrink resistant

drip dry

calendering

stain repellent

Developing a specification

Designing the technical gear for the crew of the Challenger racing yacht was just as demanding as designing the boat itself. Have a look at these specifications:

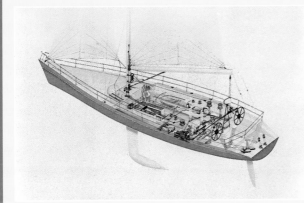

W60 Challenger
Crew: 12 max.
Displacement: 13 m tonnes
Voyage: 32 000 nautical miles
Sail area: 417 m^2
Beam: 5.25 m
Overall length: 19.5 m
Temperature range: 40°C to −20°C

Forster jacket 25026 by Henri-Lloyd
Microplex
Woven from supplex, micro-nylon yarn
Resin-backed
Teflon-coated
Hydro/stain repellent
Microfleece collar
Reflective badge and tape
Nylon non-corrosive zip

Redesigning an existing product

Designers often redesign existing products rather than starting with a totally new idea, making changes to the product while keeping it safe and efficient.

Choose an outdoor pursuits product. Put a picture of it in the centre or to one side of your page. Label the parts of the product.

Now record the following clearly:

1   The primary function of this product.
2   Which safety considerations are essential.
3   Any of the individual features that could be redesigned. Make sure this will not change its primary function or make it less safe to use. Identify these with colour or symbols.

4   What changes you could make to each of these identified features,
  a) to make it more fashionable
  b) to make it function better
  c) to make it safer.

The importance of colour

Colour can affect the function and safety of a product. Why have particular colours been used in the products you have looked at?

List other clothing and products that use colour as a safety feature. Explain how changing the colour would affect the function and safety of these products.

Experiment with changing the colour of all or part of your outdoor pursuits product to make it appear more fashionable to a target audience. You may want to use computer software that will enable you to change colours easily and quickly.

Quality assurance when manufacturing

As your design is a prototype of a product that will be made in high volume, how will a manufacturer ensure that the quality of each item is good and that they all come out the same? Draw a flow diagram to show how to produce your item, and mark on it stages when the quality should be checked.

Specialist Products Challenge 70

Checking the quality of raw materials . . . .

Checking one in five seams . . .

Checking for flaws in fabric . . .

Using a pattern as a template, make sure position is always the same . . .

Case study – protypes and manufacturing in volume

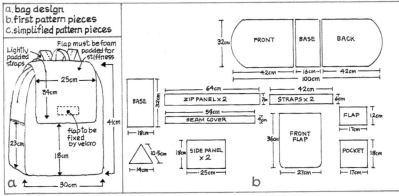

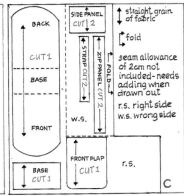

Jo, a GCSE student, designed and prototyped a back pack. But he found that the manufacture was difficult and could be improved with better planning.

'The fabric was not practical and the bag, though stylish, took too long to make. The fabric stretched when I cut it out, and it frayed easily, so it was difficult to make up the bag. The seams had to be bound to stop them fraying and it took a long time to do. I decided to make some changes to the design and the manufacture to improve it. I simplified the pattern pieces so fewer pieces were needed and used materials that required less finishing. I bought these in bulk. I also simplified the making so it is quicker and easier to make. I produced and used a plan of making, and produced a manufacturing specification to help quality control. At critical points during the manufacture I ensured quality checks.'

Look at the information opposite and think about your design and your prototype. What differences would there be if it was manufactured in high volume? Jo did this to improve his design.

Prototype of your own	High volume
Production by individual craftsperson Jo's bag was hand-made by one individual.	**Team-based production** Made by a teamworking group of specialist skilled machinists.
Limited by personal or school finances Jo's backpack was aimed at student clients. It was expensive because it was slow to make. Materials were limited by personal finances.	**Controlled by precise costings, what customer will pay and profitability** The backpack suits the needs of a wide range of users – target market students. Cheaper to make, because it can be quickly and efficiently made. The materials are cheaper because of bulk buying. Price is controlled by precise costings, resulting in a lower target price.
Quality based on individual's craft skills Quality was checked and mistakes corrected as the work progressed on Jo's bag.	**Quality reliant on control systems** Quality checked at critical points in manufacture. CAM systems used.
Hand tools mainly used Jo's bag was made using hand tools and equipment available in school.	**Greater reliance on machine tools** Made using programmable machinery, using CAD/CAM systems and control.
Quality control in hands of the designer or maker Jo used his specification as guide for quality control. He evaluated work as it progressed.	**Quality specified and controlled through use of quality systems** Uses a set manufacturing specification for quality control. Compared to a finished sample. Checks for product safety and suitability for end-use.

Be enterprising

Your challenge!

Most products are made or manufactured with the intention of them being bought by users. The designer (or the designer's client) will have identified potential users for the product. The product is then designed to meet the needs of these users. It has to be marketed to appeal to the users and make them want to buy it.

The product must then be made in sufficient quantities to meet the expected demand. **Your group's challenge** is to identify the need for a product and the group of people who might use it, and then design and manufacture the product in volume. You could set up a mini-enterprise to do this Challenge.

Why this activity is useful

◆ The Challenge will give you experience of being an entrepreneur.

◆ You will develop a greater understanding of designing and making in a business environment.

◆ You can put into practice what you have learned about manufacturing products in quantity.

◆ In most areas of business and industry you will need to work as part of a team. You will develop teamworking skills and learn about managing teams, finance, personnel, production and marketing.

The broader picture . . .

Individuals and groups of people make and manufacture products. What products are produced in your local area? Do you know people who are involved in this? What do they do?

Many companies are international and have factories in various countries. Why do you think this is so?

Manufacturing industries can use huge quantities of raw materials and resources such as electricity and water. They can also produce waste products. What steps can be taken to make manufacturing more environmentally friendly?

Everyday we are bombarded with advertisements for products. What do you think of adverts?

To be successful

You will need to:

★ identify roles for each team member

★ design a product that the user wants. Develop and make prototypes of the product to ensure that it can be manufactured easily

★ produce the product efficiently and ensure high quality

★ market the product successfully

★ cover your costs and make a profit.

Planning things through

▸ Your team will need to have regular meetings to ensure that the work is on schedule.

▸ Each team member will have to take a leading role for their area of responsibility (e.g. finance, production) and keep a clear record of what they do. Team members will need to be designers, workers and managers. The team will have to co-ordinate all activities, particularly with those running in parallel, e.g. production and marketing.

▸ Accurate costings are needed for each stage – designing, manufacturing and testing, and marketing.

Case study – Belinda Downes

Belinda Downes is a professional artist who earns her living by making embroidered cards and books. She works with book publishers and greetings card manufacturers.

Receiving the design brief

Belinda's publishers give her a subject for a book. The subject might be fairy tales or nursery rhymes for young children. At meetings with the editor and designer she discusses her ideas with them and they will add ideas of their own.

The publishers give Belinda deadlines and other information: intended audience, size, number of pages, the amount of text, page layouts. The books can take anything up to two years to produce.

Designing – the initial stage

Belinda uses her sketchbooks for inspiration and from them prepares line drawings to scale. She translates these into embroidery when they have been agreed with the publisher.

Stitching the pieces

Using hand and machine stitching techniques, the embroidered pieces take shape. She paints a lot of her fabrics and images, following the line drawing, adding beads, buttons, lace. This is her favourite part of the work and she enjoys developing the images.

What happens next

The embroidery is stretched over card, photographed and then printed on thousands of book covers, cards and products sold throughout the world.

Belinda Downes makes a one-off, but her design is suitable for manufacturing in high volumes. The embroidery looks good when reproduced on book covers, cards and other products. She also sells her finished embroidery.

Who runs a business

You can take on the various roles required to run a successful business.

What would be the best role (or roles) for each member of your team?

Think about each other's skills and abilities. But do not forget that the roles need to be flexible because of the varying workloads. A good example of a project team is:

- project manager
- finance manager
- personnel manager
- production manager
- marketing manager.

Setting yourselves up

It will be necessary to have meetings to make decisions such as what the product will be, how it will be produced and how it will be marketed. Sometimes all the group will need to meet, sometimes only two or three members will need to meet to make decisions.

Use a photocopiable sheet to keep a record of meetings. It should include the following:

- name of company
- date of meeting
- names of those attending the meeting
- the matters that are discussed
- decisions made (including any voting)
- actions to be taken.

You also need to design a method of recording all costs involved in the project, e.g. materials used, energy costs and other costs (will there be wages to pay or advertising costs?).

Your teacher will explain the costs involved. A good way to record this information is to use a spreadsheet.

There will be three main stages in making the business a success.

Stage 1 Identifying the product

- Market research – identifying a market opportunity.
- Designing the product.

Stage 2 Production

- The planning of the production process including equipment needed.
- The staff training needed.

- The manufacturing of a high quality product.
- The health and safety requirements.

Stage 3 Marketing the product

- Marketing campaign.
- Advertising.
- Distributing the product.
- Selling the product.

You will need to decide which team members will plan and organise each stage.

Remember: a number of activities in the stages can take place at the same time. Detailed planning and co-ordinating is needed!

Market research

The market is made up of sellers and buyers (users) of the product. The product you want to sell must fit as closely as possible with what the user wants. The first step then is to identify who your user is.

To help you design the product, the second step is to research what the user wants. There are two main methods of doing this – **product research** and **user research**.

Carry out the following market research:

■ Find out what products other businesses are producing.

■ Compare existing products available.

■ Test the existing products yourselves.

■ Ask potential users to test the products.

■ Provide questionnaires for the potential users.

Use your research to help you design and make a product that will be successful. Remember to choose a product that you can produce in enough quantity in the time available.

Planning for production

Describe how your product will be made by breaking the process down into specific tasks. You might want to draw a flowchart.

You are going to be making your product in high volume. Are there ways that your team could make production

■ quicker?

■ more cost effective?

■ to a higher quality?

This group of students decided that they could change the way they worked. To make it quicker they used some ready-made components. To make it more cost effective they used CAM so that the products came out perfectly each time.

To make it better for themselves they shared out the repetitive jobs and changed jobs regularly. This was not quicker, but they were much happier and the quality of the finished products was better.

What are the most suitable methods of production for your product?

Which production method suits the facilities and resources available to you?

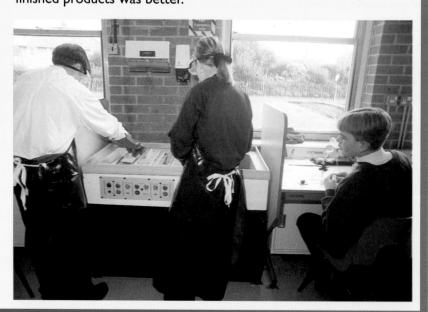

Quality assurance

To achieve high quality in the manufacturing of your product, you will need to implement quality assurance during all the stages of designing and making.

Quality assurance is achieved by checking that everything is done correctly at each stage. There are three main principles to follow:

■ Right first time, everytime!

■ Constantly aim to improve and innovate the products!

■ Always look to exceed user expectation!

This can be achieved through accurate measuring, inspection and testing, use of jigs, moulds and templates and by using remote control devices such as CAD/CAM equipment.

quality assurance	food	graphics	resistant materials	textiles	electronic products
Accurate measuring	Measuring scoops for ingredients	Use of scale when designing	Marking out of materials	Mixing dyes	Using multimeter to check voltages
Inspection and testing	Choosing ingredients	Testing colours	Testing strength of components	Inspecting the finish of a test piece	Check for dry joints
Jigs, moulds and templates	Shape cutter or mould	Drawing template	Drilling jig	Printing stencils	Using a PCB mask
Systems and control (including CAD/CAM)	Conveyor oven	Plotter cutter	CNC lathe	CNC sewing machine	Plotting PCB mask Drilling holes for components

What further examples can you add to each box in the chart above?

What quality assurance methods could you use in the designing and making of your product? You could add these to your production plan.

What training will team members need?

Specialist Products Challenge 70

Marketing the product

You need to plan your marketing campaign well in advance. Cover the following:

■ Price – could you use introductory offers?

■ Packaging – needs to be eye-catching but functional and safe.

■ How and where to sell – personal contact, door-to-door, shop, mail order, to a retailer.

■ Type of advertising – posters, leaflets, magazines, radio or TV advert.

A marketing campaign uses a variety of ways to advertise the product

Designing and manufacturing

This second part of this book will help you to develop the designing and making skills you need to carry out the assignments in the first part. It looks closely at various aspects of designing and making that are developed further in the other *Challenges* books.

You may use some of these pages with your teacher when learning more about designing and making.

Remember – you should *always* turn to this section *before* asking your teacher for help when you are designing or making and are not sure what to do next.

One of the most important things you should be learning in Design and Technology is to work independently – having your **own** ideas, developing them in your **own** way, understanding for yourself **what** you are doing, and **why** you are doing it that particular way.

Contents

Designing and manufacturing

Planning and managing your project

Planning your work carefully will help to make sure that it goes well. Good planning will make sure that:
- you use your time well
- tasks are completed in the best possible order and on time
- materials and equipment are available when you need them
- you can take responsibility for your own work.

How to plan your project

List all of the main tasks that need to be done. Add any other tasks that are related to these main tasks.

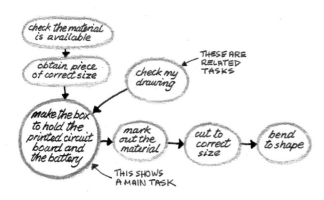

Use these questions to help plan the tasks:
1 Which tasks must be done first?
2 Which tasks can be done together?
3 Which tasks depend on others being done first?
4 What materials and equipment are needed for each task?
5 How long will each task take?
6 How long have you got for the complete project?

Putting the tasks in order

For each task ask yourself:
- What do I need to do before this?
- What do I need to do after this?
- What can I do at the same time as this?

Ways of planning

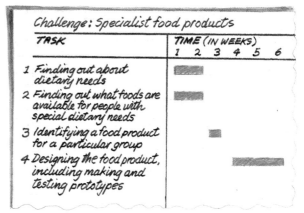

Part of a time plan chart

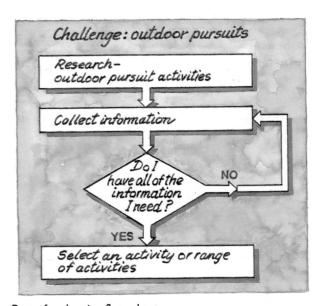

Part of a planning flow chart

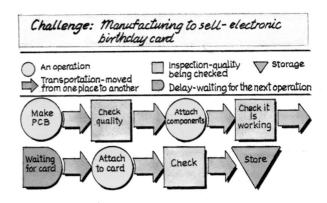

Using a production plan

Forward planning

Good planning can also be used to prevent things going wrong or to help find solutions when they do. Using these questions for each main task will help you:

◆ What could go wrong with this task?
◆ What effect might this have?
◆ How can I prevent it going wrong?
◆ What other ways are there of doing it?

Evaluation

Designing involves continuously making judgements about needs, ideas, how to do things, etc. All these are **evaluations**. You will be evaluating continuously throughout your designing and making, especially by thinking about the quality of your work as it progresses. At key points you should ask yourself questions about your work. This will help you to make decisions about your designing and making.

Evaluation also includes the 'end testing' of products; this is covered within the individual Challenges in this book.

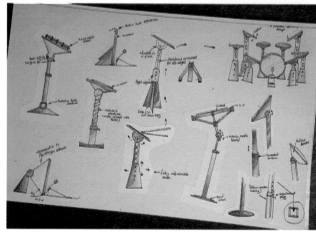

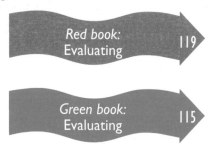

Red book:
Evaluating 119

Green book:
Evaluating 115

There are many techniques that you can use to evaluate your work. At all of the key points in your project you should obtain the opinions of other people, and of your clients if you are designing for them.

Designers often make notes on their drawings **to evaluate their ideas**; these are known as **annotations**. Annotations can show what other ideas were considered, how the design might develop, modifications that you have considered and what other people, including the client, thought of the ideas. Giving the reasons for these will reveal your own evaluation of your ideas.

As you develop your design and **use models and prototypes** to check that your design meets the specification, the decisions you make will rely on evaluations.

Checklists are a very useful tool for evaluating as you work. You can include all of the constraints from the design brief and specification in the checklist. You should also include the questions that you ask your clients if you are designing for other people.

As you are **making your product** it is also important that you evaluate all of the stages of

manufacture. This will include:
- using a manufacturing specification and checking your work against it
- using a production or manufacturing plan and checking your work against it
- checking that calculations are correct before you start
- checking that tools and equipment are in good working order
- using templates and other 'checking tools'
- checking your measurements
- checking each stage of production before going on to the next
- checking the correct fitting of components before you fix them permanently.

When evaluating your designing and making, you need to give yourself time to think about what you are doing. This will allow you to make the best possible product that answers your design brief.

Good quality products rely on good quality evaluation.

Designing for users, clients and manufacturers

When developing a new product, a designer may be working for one company but he or she will need to also act on behalf of others such as companies and individuals. This is likely to involve:
- the people who will be buying the product
- the people who will be using the product
- the company that will manufacture the product
- the company that is paying them to design it.

Green book: Identifying needs 90

All designing involves choices between different ways that a product might be made, how it might be used, its value for money, how durable (long lasting) it will be, etc. When designers make decisions, they have to weigh up which aspects are most important. Sometimes these will be set out in a clear specification, but even then the personal views of the designer will inevitably affect their design approaches. One designer might always take environmental issues so seriously that they limit the choice of materials they are prepared to use. Another might be so interested in how a product works that this might be (perhaps an unintentional) priority. Another might have such a strong concern for the appearance of products that their work always concentrates on it.

Entrepreneurs

Developing a new product requires time, and time is money. Someone has to be imaginative and adventurous enough to pay for the investment in time, materials and manufacturing costs up front – before the product goes on sale and money starts coming in. Who provides this investment? Sometimes it is an established company that invests some of the profits from existing products in developing new ones. Sometimes it is an inventor or designer who comes up with a new idea and wants to see it reach the market. They may be helped by a bank or a **venture capitalist** who puts money (**capital**) into new projects in the expectation that they will share in the future profits.

However it is done, new product development involves some investment in advance and the risk that a loss will be made rather than a profit. The bigger the possible profit, the greater the possible loss is likely to be.

Things to do 1

1 List and sketch three products, one of each of the following:
   ◆ one that was or is really new and successful
   ◆ one that was really new but unsuccessful
   ◆ one that was not really very new, but was clearly successful.
2 Add notes to each to say:
   ◆ in what ways the product was or was not new
   ◆ in what ways it was successful
   ◆ whether a lot of investment was needed to develop the product, or if it needed less investment.

The people (usually working for a company) who are making the initial investment to develop a new product will probably want a strong say in how it is designed. Also, the designer has to try to balance his or her own views and preferences with the demands of others. These people may be involved with the product in other ways, from those who make it to those who have to deal with it as rubbish for disposal or recycling.

The people who will be buying the product

Many products are bought by the people who will use them. This is typical of 'consumer products', those designed for use by ordinary people. But a designer has to remember that many of these products are bought as gifts, so must appeal to the giver as well as the receiver. This will affect, for example, whether it looks expensive or attractive. The presents we give others tell them something about us and also about how we value them. For example, expensive perfumes are all about making people feel special, particularly if the perfumes are a gift. The packaging helps them to look expensive and important.

Things to do 2

Collect some examples of packages from different products, paste them on a board and comment on what each package is saying about the person who buys the product.

When you are designing a product for sale you must consider its appeal to the buyers, whether or not they will be the users.

The people who will be using the product

Many products are bought by employers for their employees to use. Do they get the best? Sometimes they do and the employees may feel that their company is valuing them highly by providing the best tools for their job. Sometimes employees are provided with more or better than they need as part of their 'remuneration package' – what they get paid and what 'perks' they get. Are you provided with anything that tells you that someone values you highly?

Things to do 3

Talk to some adults and try to find somebody whose 'pay' for their job includes extra perks, such as a mobile phone or a company car for use in their own time. Also talk to someone who feels undervalued by what they are given to do their job with. Why do they feel this way?

When you are designing a product for sale you must consider its appeal to the users, whether or not they will be the buyers.

The company that will manufacture the product

Sometimes design companies develop products and pay other companies to manufacture the products for them to sell.

Case study – Atkinson Design Associates

Designer Paul Atkinson's product, TEXT, consists of a range of tables for offices, conference rooms and reception areas, based on a rather special fitting holding the legs to the table tops' frames. Atkinson Design Associates had been designing office furniture for many years, but they wanted to 'do something properly' for once and also to hold the design copyrights themselves.

TEXT was primarily aimed at successful businesses such as financial services, blue chip organisations and high-tech companies, many of which were moving their offices to cities such as London, Edinburgh and Manchester. Despite being a small company, Atkinson Design Associates undertook all aspects of the new product's development including design, manufacture, and the launch and advertising of the range.

Being entrepreneurial like this costs money. The design of this type of item typically takes an investment of over £125 000. Atkinson reduced this but other work in the company suffered as a result. The initial investment in special tools to manufacture the product was £30 000. Marketing and distribution costs often total three or four times the design and development costs.

TEXT products have been successful and several major companies have bought them. One year after the launch, Atkinson Design Associates have covered the costs of their investment and are starting to make a profit on the products. This was sooner than they had expected. Two more products are now under development to complement TEXT and to increase Atkinson's presence in the office furniture market.

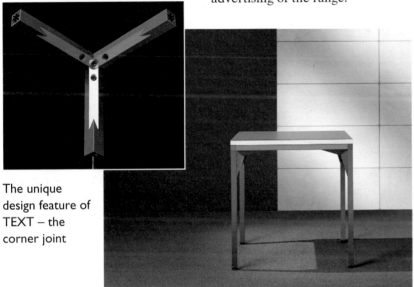

The unique design feature of TEXT – the corner joint

A typical office table

More often, designers either work permanently for the company that is developing the new product or they are **commissioned** (paid just for the development work on that project). Either way, they have to consider how the product will be made and whether this will be cost-effective. That is, whether the costs involved in manufacturing will be recovered in sales. Sometimes this means a high risk. For example, they might need a new, and possibly expensive, production method to make the

product more attractive. They hope this will cause it to sell very well.

The company that is paying them to design it

Companies that pay designers to develop new products can vary very much in their approach, from being very cautious and only working on the type of product they are familiar with, to being very adventurous. There is always a risk though – even cautious developments can go very wrong.

Things to think about when designing

Moral issues and social values

Products are developed to meet people's needs. This can happen when opportunities for new or improved products have been seen. They are developed to meet what companies hope people will want – to fill what they see as a gap in the market. Decisions that influence the design of these products, the way they are made and how they are marketed are based on a balance between many different issues. These include technical, economic, aesthetic, environmental and moral issues. The decisions are also influenced by personal, social and cultural values – the views held by those involved.

> The broader picture . . . in any Challenge

> Red book:
> Aesthetics 112
> The environment 114

> Green book: Safety 99
> Costs 100
> Human factors 103

> Costing and prices 99

Values are people's beliefs about what is right and what is wrong. Individuals use their values to make personal judgements. **Social values** are held by groups of people and represent what is in the best interests of the majority not just a small minority.

Different groups of people and different societies have their own set of values. These **cultural values** may be different from other groups and are often based on religious and other similar sets of ideas.

Things to do 4

Look at the pictures of toys and answer these questions. (You can look through catalogues for other types of toys.)

◆ Who do you think would use each toy? What makes you think that?
◆ Do you think any of these toys encourage a particular sort of behaviour?
◆ Does each toy appeal to a wide range of children from different backgrounds or only to particular children?
◆ Do any of the toys appeal to both boys and girls?
◆ Are any particular values attached to each toy?
◆ Could any of the toys cause offence to people with certain values?

Alternatively you could watch some television advertisements for toys and use the same set of questions.

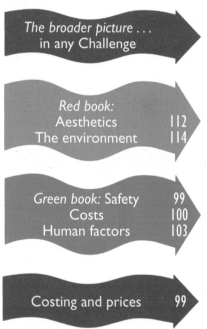

Use the following questions to help you take account of values issues in your own project:

◆ What is the user group for your product?
◆ What are the values of this group of people?
◆ How does your product take account of these values?
◆ Could your product offend other people with different values?

Keeping an eye on costs and thinking about prices

When you are making choices during designing and manufacturing you need to think about your costs. You can make savings by selecting your materials wisely and by using them carefully so that you avoid waste and make the most of what is available.

Green book:
Thinking about costs   100

You need to make sure that you do not run out of money because you spent too much or made costly mistakes early on in your project. Your costs may also mount up as you go along and the total amount that you spend may come as a surprise if you are not careful.

Spreadsheets are being used here to predict costs and to compare the effect of using different materials and components for seats at George Ward School

Keep an eye on the total cost of your product by planning and estimating before you start making.

It is important to work cost-effectively and make savings where possible. If you intend customers to buy your products you must also plan to sell them at the right price. Setting this selling price has to be done with great care. If you intend to recover your costs so that you can make more of your products for sale, you will need to make a profit.

Decisions on prices need to be made carefully. Too high a price may mean that customers prefer a cheaper product so you will sell less. Then you may not make a profit. Too low a price may mean that you do not fully recover your costs, so make a loss.

In industry, companies often consider a 'four-layer lolly' when setting a product price.

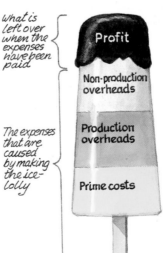

what is left over when the expenses have been paid } **Profit**

e.g. The amount left of the selling price after all of the expenses have been paid

Non-production overheads

e.g. Rent charged on the warehouse, shops, some people's wages, advertising

The expenses that are caused by making the ice-lolly {

Production overheads

e.g. Cost of keeping the lollies frozen, warehousing, transport to the shops

Prime costs

e.g. The cost of what is actually used to make the ice-lolly, including water, sugar, colouring, flavouring, electricity for freezing the ice, the stick, the wrapper and all the wages paid to the people who actually make the lolly

Manufacturers have to add up all their costs carefully before setting the selling price. This shows some of the things that they have to bear in mind

Manufacturing   116

Things to do 5

If you are supplying your product to a customer you need to work out what price you will charge. Draw a lolly for your own product. What are the layers that you will need to bear in mind when working out your selling price?

After you have worked out this price your client asks you to reduce this by 20% but insists that you maintain the same level of quality. Work out how you could achieve this.

Case study – Döhler (UK) Ltd

Döhler produce components used to make food products. These components are sold to other companies which use them to manufacture the foods. Many of the components are foods or starches with emulsifiers which, when mixed with water, give different effects. This is rather like using a packet cake mix on a large scale. One market in which Döhler is very active is desserts for airline meals. Bruce Toon, describes what must be considered when a client asks Döhler to develop an airline dessert. They usually include a cost per portion breakdown in their specification.

RECIPE

1 Döhler Dark Souffle Cup
2 g Chopped hazelnuts
35g Hazelnut Mousse

Hazelnut mousse

400g Döhler Mousse All-in-One Hazelnut
1000g Cold milk

Whisk together for approx 5 mins.
Pipe into cup and decorate.

'Before we begin there are a number of points to be considered:
- the size of the container the dessert will be served in
- the shape of the container
- whether the dessert will be the same shape as the container or different
- the space available on the meal tray
- whether the cutlery to be used is plastic or metal.

'Usually we will make a presentation to the client, taking samples of the types of dessert we can produce within the price range and specification. This example for a Chocolate Cup with Hazelnut Mousse shows the detailed costings of the desserts.

'Accurate costing of ingredients is important as the client is able to see how much each portion will cost each time it is made. The components may be supplied to the manufacturer or Döhler can supply frozen ready-made desserts.'

Costings for Chocolate Cup with Hazelnut Mousse (40 portions)

Ingredients	Amount	Cost
Döhler Dark Soufflé Cup	40	£8.00
All in One Hazelnut Mousse	400g	£2.17
Cold milk	1000g	£0.76
Chopped hazelnuts	92g	£0.64
Total		£11.57
Cost per portion		£0.29

Designing for product maintenance

When you design your product you need to think about the maintenance it may need.

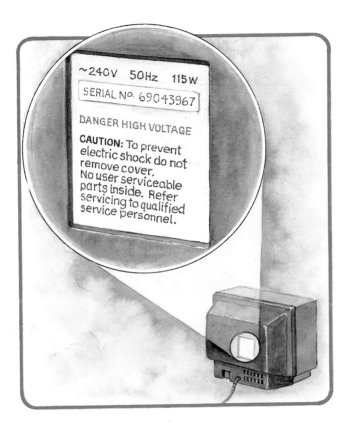

~240V 50Hz 115W
SERIAL No. 69043967
DANGER HIGH VOLTAGE
CAUTION: To prevent electric shock do not remove cover. No user serviceable parts inside. Refer servicing to qualified service personnel.

Do you need to provide instructions to make sure that the product is used correctly and safely?

Do you need to supply spares?

Designing for product life

How long do you want your product to last?

Green Book: Thinking about function 97

SLICED HAM

DISPLAY UNTIL
08JULY

USE BY
10JULY

KEEP REFRIGERATED

INGREDIENTS: Pork, Salt, Dextrose, Sodium Polyphosph, Antioxidant (Sodium

1002 1533

All food products have a shelf-life

Green book: Thinking about safety 99

Is your product to be used only once or repeatedly?

When you design your product, you need to think about how long you want it to last. This will affect the quality of the product and the materials and components or ingredients you use.

Inclusive designing

Designs that meet the inclusive criteria are awarded the Owl Mark

'Design for the young and you exclude the old. Design for the old and you include the young.' This statement sums up the idea of inclusive designing. When you are designing your own product it is important to keep this idea in your mind. Keep asking yourself the questions:

◆ Who are you designing for?
◆ Do they have special needs?
◆ Are these needs shared by others?
◆ Who should benefit from this product?
◆ Who else could benefit from this product?

Designing for target groups

Sometimes designers consider the needs of a specific group very closely. A really important part of the design process is the consideration of who is going to use the product.

Sometimes it is essential to design for a target group. However, this can limit the range of people that will use the product.

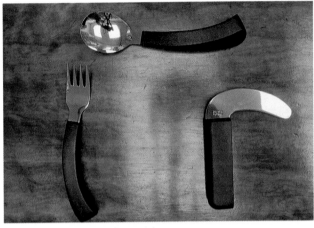

Most people would be unhappy using the cutlery above designed especially for weak (e.g. elderly or infirm) people but it helps that target group very much

Case study – Patricia Moore

Patricia dressed as an 85-year-old

Patricia as she really is

Patricia Moore spent three years travelling through the USA and Canada disguised as an 85-year-old. She not only dressed as an old woman she also restricted her joints, hearing and vision. The discoveries she made shaped her thinking about design and were influential on the growing universal design movement in the USA.

Things to do 6

Consider these extremes of use in your designing. Observe an elderly or a very young person:

◆ How do they communicate or make their views known?
◆ How and what do they eat and drink at mealtimes?
◆ How do they move around?
◆ How do they entertain themselves?

Visiting an old people's home and/or a nursery could be a valuable source of research. You could try a role-play situation like Patricia Moore, where you use your design as if you were elderly or a child.

Things to do 7

Big Time

Freehand tray with non-slip mat

Capstan tap turner

Helping hands

Identifying the needs of very specialist groups can lead to important developments in products or materials. The items shown above were designed to help people recovering from an illness, elderly people and people with various disabilities. Considering the needs of one particular group can very often improve your design for everyone else too. How do these meet the 'inclusive design' criteria?

Find your own examples of products that have been designed for specific groups of people. You could look at food products, electronics products, products for use around the home and garden, clothing and other textiles products, and graphic products.

Answer these questions:
◆ Which features are 'client specific'?
◆ Which features are general design features?

Designing for specific groups

Sometimes it is necessary to design for a small specialist group because they have specific needs. These needs should be made clear in your specification.

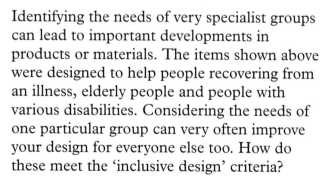

Collapsible Structures
Challenge
62

A designer's checklist

The more people you can interest in your design, the more of your product you are likely to sell. This means that you are likely to earn more from the product. It also leads to better products.

You can use this checklist with your own designs:
◆ Who could use this product?
◆ Who couldn't use this product? Does this matter?
◆ Who would want to use this product?
◆ Who could benefit from using this product?
◆ Who is excluded from using this product? Does this matter?
◆ What can you do to make your product more useful to more people?

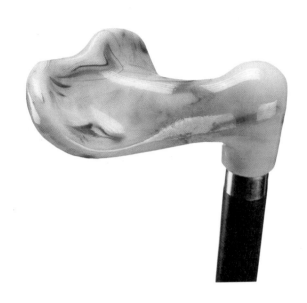

A walking stick designed especially for those with poor grip

Graphics in designing

This section provides examples that show how to use graphic media during the different stages of designing:
◆ recording your thoughts and inspirations
◆ developing your ideas further
◆ planning for production
◆ presenting your finished ideas.

You need to choose the best methods for the different stages of your design work.

Graphics used to record ideas

'. . . good design is a hit-or-miss process, with many false starts, abandoned ideas and failed explorations. In many ways, the journey is as significant as the destination.'
Nick Butcher, Design Director, Rodney Fitch and Co

You must develop the habit of recording your design explorations – your journey to a final design. Often you will want to make a record of something you thought of, or something you have seen, to use at a later time. Freehand line drawings with pencil or pen are the quickest, simplest way of doing this and it is useful to keep them in a sketchbook so that they do not get lost.

Students' sketch books

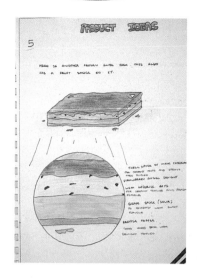

These sketches show what a food product will look like on the inside. They give a good idea of the textures created

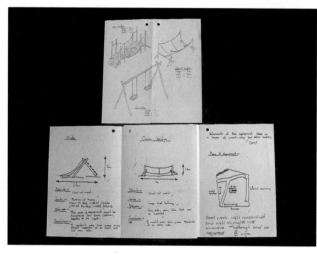

This student has recorded details of a research visit to a children's play area using freehand sketches

Another quick method of recording is to use existing pictures to create a cut and paste collage. A collage can be used to set a mood, contrast styles or to show a range of similar products.

Simple line drawings can communicate your ideas clearly and provide a starting point for further design development.

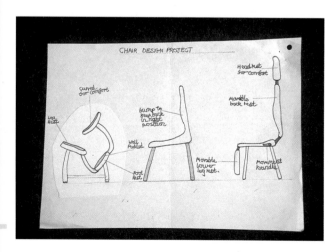

If you need to record in more detail, rendering can be used to show texture, light and shade and colour.

Red book:
Rendering   102

DESIGNING AND MANUFACTURING

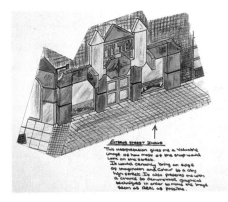

Graphics in developing ideas

When developing ideas you have to be creative to think up the best ways of communicating your ideas. Often this will mean combining various media as well as different methods of drawing. These examples show students developing their ideas for textiles using a variety of graphic media.

Students' use of graphics to develop their textiles designs

Following the sketching of their ideas, students have developed their work using simple paper patterns to produce repeat designs and fabric pens to colour the material

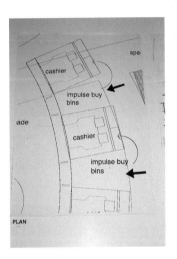

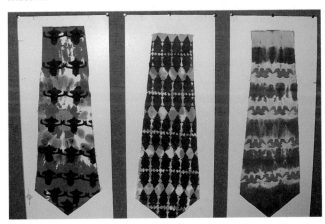

Between them these two drawings make the layout and the appearance of these checkout tills clear

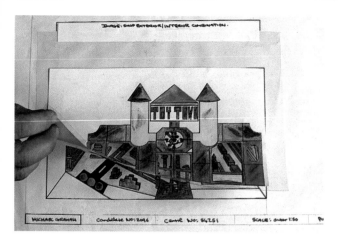

Red book:
Drawing your ideas   98

Graphics in production planning

Accurate drawings should to be produced to communicate the information needed to make all the parts of the product. These are usually drawn using **orthographic projection** or **isometric projection**. They can be drawn freehand but where precision is required they are drawn to scale using drawing instruments or using computer aided drafting.

Red book:
Orthographic projection   99

This student has used transparent overlays, and photos with line drawing and colour rendering to create a very effective presentation

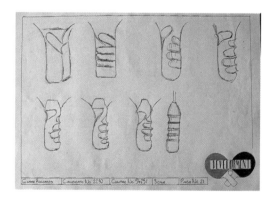

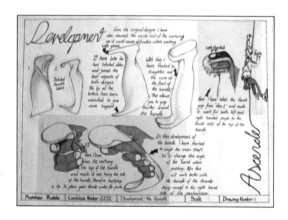

Another good method is to use a colour 'wash' to emphasise parts of a drawing. This use of colour clearly shows how the hand would fit the handle of this 'Climbing Ascender' design

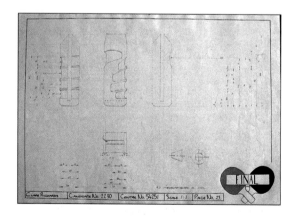

A student's orthographic drawings

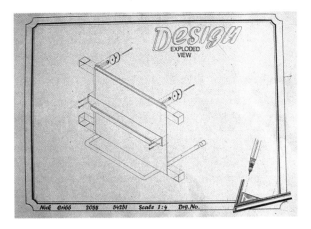

A student's isometric drawing

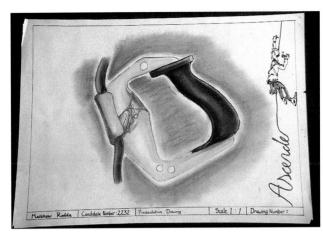

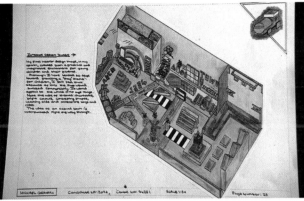

Colour rendered scale drawings

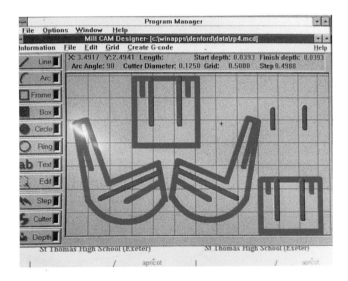

CAD used in production planning

What information will you show in which type of drawing?

Graphics to present ideas

To present your finished ideas you may need to use a further stage of accurate drawings. These are often drawn to scale and are likely to include colour rendering to show what the finished products will look like. These types of drawing are used when presenting work to a user or client.

An important part of presenting your work deals with layout and composition. You should always try to present your work to a high standard. Good designers present all their work well, as can be seen in the sketch examples above.

This type of work will include the layout of graphics and text, use of borders, title boxes and possibly motifs and logos.

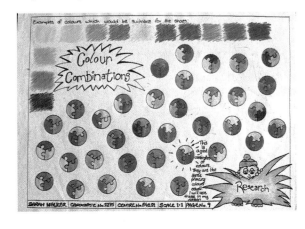

Good **composition** (the way the elements of a picture are put together) requires some clear space to ensure that the design is not cluttered. Simple, decisive approaches work best.

Desk top publishing (DTP) is an excellent way of designing the page layouts for your design folio.

Evaluating products and applications

Products in the home 1: Small-scale products

Often small-scale products that we use every day are not as simple as they seem. They are often clever, high performance products. We use and take for granted many objects without thinking about how they work, how they are manufactured or how they are designed. We have a wide experience and knowledge of these products that we do not make use of.

Things to do 8

Look in a small storage area in your house such as a medicine or bathroom cabinet, a desk, a tool box or a kitchen drawer. Examine some of the items you find there to try to understand how they work and how they are used.

◆ What materials is it made of?
◆ Why have those materials been chosen?
◆ How has it been made or manufactured?
◆ What processes were used to make it?
◆ What features does it have?
◆ How are these features helpful to the user?
◆ What scientific principles have been used in the product? For example, ways of storing or transferring energy, ways of providing the force needed, electrical safety.
◆ Have any recent developments in technology been used in the product? For example, new materials or electronics. How has it been used? Has this 'new technology' resulted in improvements to the product?

Discuss your answers with your teacher and class.

Are these objects as simple as they look?

Products in the home 2: Analysing an everyday activity

In order to improve a product it is important to understand what for, how, when, how often and where it is used. This helps designers find and solve problems when designing a product; they can modify or redesign it to create a better product. Products are constantly being redesigned to improve their performance.

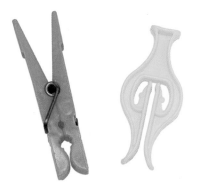

This photograph shows how the design of a clothes peg has been changed to make it cheaper to manufacture and easier to use. The newer design is a one-piece injection moulding. The older design has two injection moulded pieces and a wire spring

When you are next using a tool or a piece of equipment, preparing a recipe, cleaning your teeth or any other everyday activity think about these questions:

◆ What are you doing?
◆ What equipment are you using?
◆ How are you using it?
◆ Could it be made to do this job better?
◆ How could it be improved?
◆ Would these improvements benefit you only or other people as well?

Products in the home 3: One-off or volume production?

Different products are made in very different numbers. You may have a cupboard or work surface in your kitchen that was made specially to fit an awkward space. There is probably no other like it anywhere; it is a **one-off**. Ball-point pens are made in vast numbers and every one that comes off the production line is exactly the same as all the others. We call this **high volume production**. High quality fountain pens are made in much smaller numbers; this is known as **low volume production**.

Things to do 9

Many food products are made in high volumes. You can buy cook-chill and frozen meals. For example, Italian foods such as lasagne and pizza are popular. The same products could be made at home following your own recipe.

You can buy a sweater from a large store or you can knit your own. The one you make yourself would be a one-off. You will probably use a pattern to knit the sweater; this means that a small batch of the same size or several sweaters of different sizes could be made.

Cups, saucers, plates and so on are usually produced in high volumes. You may have some ceramic products such as ornaments that were individually designed and made or produced in small numbers.

Compare the home made and high volume products using these questions:

◆ The design of the product – how is it suitable for low volume or high volume production?
◆ The costs of making the product – what are the costs of the materials, labour, equipment and so on?
◆ The equipment and tools used to make the product – are they general purpose or specialist tools?
◆ Who determines the quality of the finished product? How is the level of quality maintained?

Choose one other product in your home, at school or related to your own interests that you think could be manufactured either in low volume or high volume. Describe the product using the questions above.

Products in the home 4: An historical perspective

The development of new technologies means that we can design new products. You will know how quickly products can become out of date. A good example of this is computer technology; new computers are only up-to-date for about three or four years.

1991

1996

Why do you think computers have changed so much in such a short space of time?

It can be very interesting to trace the developments in a product over a period of time. You will be amazed by some of the changes in materials and manufacturing technology that you will see.

Things to do 10

Choose a product that interests you. Use your school library and other resources to find out how it has changed and developed over time.

Look at the product now and in the past and describe:
◆ the materials and components used
◆ the way the product was manufactured
◆ how the design reflects the fashions of the time
◆ any technological developments that have been used in the product.

Products in the High Street

Have a look in some shops next weekend. Have you ever considered that when you are out shopping you are making decisions about design? Whether you are making an important purchase or just 'window shopping' you are forming opinions about how well products have been designed.

When faced with the choices that are available in the High Street, how do you decide which to buy?

You are often faced with a bewildering range of alternatives

Things to do 11

1. Choose an item that you might buy or would like to buy in the near future.
2. Make a list of all the things that you consider to be important in your choice of product.
3. Sort the list into order with the most important point at the top of the list.
4. Use a catalogue to identify three products that seem to meet the points on your list.
5. Use the list to choose the one you would buy.
6. Use graphics to present to your friends the reasons why you chose that product.

Developing products: new materials and new technologies

The development of new materials and technologies allows designers to achieve things that were not possible before. Although you will be familiar with modern materials you might not be able to recognise them as easily as materials such as woods and metals.

Through the use of a fabric with 'microcellular' structure (Gore-Tex or Sympatex), fabric designers have been able to create garments that allow moisture from the body to escape but keep the rain from coming in, leaving the wearer much more comfortable

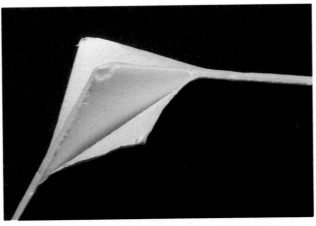

This foam board is a **composite** made of two materials. The foam core makes it light in weight and rigid whilst the paper provides a smooth surface that a graphic designer can use. Does the paper on the outside make the foam core stronger? Does the foam core make the paper stronger?

Where different materials are used together to make a new combined material the end product is called a **composite material**. These materials can have very different properties from those of the constituent materials. Usually they combine the properties of each of their **component materials** (those that they are made from). Together they are often better than any of the component materials on their own. Products made of layers of materials like this are called **laminates**.

In the aerofoil (wing) shown you can see how the polystyrene foam is encased in a carbon fibre shell. This allows very complex shapes to be made that are strong, rigid and very light. What properties do you think come from the different component materials? Think how much heavier this form would be in wood.

An aerofoil made from a carbon fibre reinforced plastics skin with a plastics foam fill

Things to do 12

Find some products made from composite materials. Laminates in particular are quite common and don't forget textiles. Explain what properties the component materials provide. Explain why they have been used in that product.

Green book:
Thinking about materials 105

Have you noticed how weak a fizzy drinks can is when it is empty? Someone once said they were made of 'drink-reinforced aluminium'! What is it that makes them strong when full?

Designing prototypes for manufacture

If you are designing a product that might be manufactured in quantity it is worth asking yourself three questions:

◆ Is it good enough for manufacturing?
◆ Can it be manufactured efficiently?
◆ How will it be manufactured?

You will need to ask these questions about each component of the product. Making working models and a prototype can help you to answer these questions.

Working models (sometimes called 'lash-ups') do not look like the final design but test how the design will work. They can be used at any stage of the design process to try out ideas. They are particularly useful for anything that moves, for example, in mechanical, electronic or pneumatic systems. You might find that some of your ideas just cannot be made to work and you need to know this before you commit yourself.

A prototype will be made towards the end of the design process. For most or all of your work in school this will probably be the last stage of your work. You will not often have the time, facilities or resources to turn your prototype into a number of final manufactured products.

In modern manufacturing, many of these processes can now be carried out using computer generated 'prototypes' that behave just as if they were real models. They can be tested against the specification and modified,

or the specification changed to make them work as well as possible.

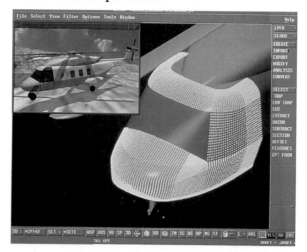

Result of an aerodynamic analysis of the nose of an NH90 helicopter. Modelling of a surface by optimising a cloud of points with 'CATIA Cloud to Geometry Optimisation (picture courtesy of NATO Helicopter Industries)'

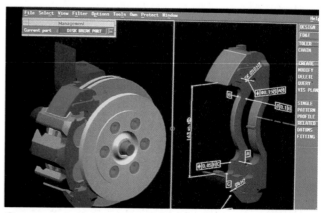

Geometric and dimensional tolerancing of 3D parts based on assembly specifications according to international standards with 'CATIA 3D Functional Dimensioning and Tolerancing'

Is it good enough for manufacturing?

Prototypes are used to discuss the design of a product with clients and also to obtain the opinions of other people. The prototype can be tested to make sure that its performance and behaviour meet the specification. Safety features and potential problems can be checked.

Obtaining the opinion of potential users.

You can also use your prototype to obtain the opinions of potential users.

If the product seems to be worth manufacturing, this is the time to think about protecting your ideas with a patent or copyright.

Can it be manufactured and how?

Working prototypes need to be made so that they represent the final product as closely as possible. Making the prototype will enable you to try out different materials, ingredients, components, manufacturing processes and finishes.

You can use the prototype to work out how you can reduce costs by cutting down the number of different parts or components used, or by improving the steps in the manufacturing process. You can also work out how to use standard components rather than ones manufactured specially for that product.

Working out how to manufacture the product.

Things to do 13

When you have completed your prototype (even if you are not going beyond that), work out ways that would allow you to reduce the costs of manufacturing a batch. Can you reduce the number of parts or components? Can you replace any of the parts you had to make by standard components? Could you change the manufacturing process to make production easier?

Introduction to manufacturing

This section will help you to plan and carry out your manufacturing. Why is it called 'Manufacturing'? In Design and Technology you will be making models and prototypes, and sometimes you will make a batch of products that are the same as each other. We will call this manufacturing. This section is intended to help you to understand better the world of manufacturing industry outside school and relate it to your work in school.

This will mean that you can develop your ideas with volume production in mind as well as creating one-offs for personal use.

Green book:
Making products in quantity 120

Products are made and manufactured in many different and interesting ways. Some products are manufactured in very large quantities while others may only need to be made once.

Only one birthday hat was made but many thousands of crash helmets have been produced for cyclists all over the world

When large numbers of the same product are made, the manufacturer has to make sure that every one of them will work properly when needed.

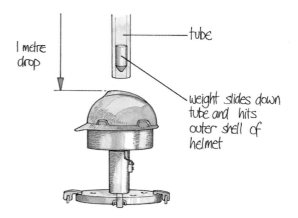

Millions of hard hats are made every year. It is important that every single one of them works properly when it is needed

OEMs (original equipment manufacturers) are the companies that produce a product. But manufacturing companies may not produce all or every part of a product, even though their own brand name appears on it.

How many products are you manufacturing?

It helps to be as clear as possible about your manufacturing intentions. When planning your product some questions to ask are:

◆ How many identical products will be made?

These bags have to be manufactured in very large numbers for PC World's customers

◆ What tools and equipment are available and which would be best for my product?

Choosing appropriate tools and processes that are easy to repeat is helpful if you are going to make more than one identical product

◆ Will my product be sold and, if so, what price do I need to charge to recover my costs?

Costs and prices   99

◆ Is my product needed straight away or will it be stored? If it is food, do I need to think about its 'shelf life'?
◆ If a higher volume is being made, how can I make sure that every product is up to quality?

Because higher volumes mean making more or many products it will also help you to think about these questions before you begin:
◆ Is my product worth manufacturing in quantity?
◆ Can it be manufactured in quantity?
◆ If so, how could it be manufactured?

Quality of design, quality of manufacture

As buyers of products (consumers) we can consider all the *Things to think about when designing* to judge whether something is well designed. But it is also likely to be important for us to judge how well made a product is. A good design may fail if poorly made and a

well made product is pointless if not also well designed.

A poorly made product may not work, it may not last long or it may simply be unpleasant to look at or feel. Quality assurance, making sure that products to be sold are of a consistently high standard, is therefore very important to both manufacturer and customer.

How do we decide whether a product is well made? When we go around shops to buy something we often look at it and feel it to decide.

Well made products

Can you recognise when a product has been made well? What do you look for? Is the way products look as important as the way they work?

This kettle was designed by Philippe Starck in 1991 and was aimed at the style-conscious European market. Imagine how different it could look if it were not well made; it would appeal to nobody

Almost every household in the country owns a kettle, but this kettle may look unusual to many people. What do you think? Is it good quality? How would the quality of its design compare with the quality of its manufacture?

The Design Council said: 'Hot Bertaa is very stylish but difficult to use. It's heavy to lift, splutters when it pours, and the handle/spout gets very hot and lets steam escape.

'The body of the kettle is cast from aluminium. The handle/spout is injection moulded in polyamide plastics and joined to the body with a bolt. The quality of the production appears very high and this is reflected in the price of around £130.'

Is there a problem with the kettle? If so, is it a problem with the quality of design or the quality of manufacture? Would you buy one?

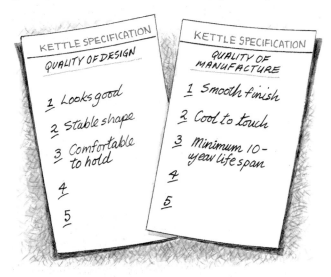

Copy these two lists and discuss the last criterion on the design specification with your friends. Add as many points as you can to the lists to help you remember the differences between them

Is having a stylish product more important than how well it works? Or is the function more important than the appearance?

A cut above the rest

Everyday products use different materials and manufacturing processes. Look at the scissors above.

Even if they are all well designed, how would poor manufacture make either of them a less good product? Compare their handles:

◆ Might they fit a hand well, are they smooth?
◆ Are there any uncomfortable projections?
◆ Does the quality of manufacture make them look attractive?

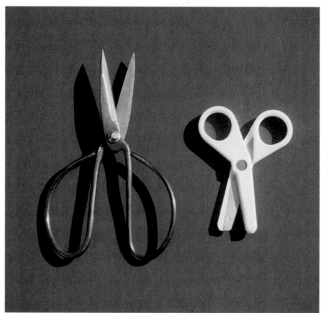

These scissors can be compared for their quality of design as well as their quality of manufacture

As a buyer we might like to know lots of other things, such as:
◆ Do they work well?
◆ Will they stay sharp?
◆ Will they bend or break?
◆ Will they go rusty?
◆ Are they good value for money?

Of course, you would need to use these scissors to make a real comparison. You could get others in your class to bring in sets of similar products to compare such as pairs of trainers.

These are all successful products. Do you think that both the quality of design and the quality of manufacture is high on each one?

To create high quality manufactured products we have to think carefully about the quality of their design and the quality of their manufacture. Both influence the eventual quality of the finished product.

When designers understand how things are produced and work closely with the manufacturers who produce them, better products are likely. Why is this? Why will this be important for you?

Planning your manufacturing

Before you begin to manufacture a product ask yourself, what jobs need to be done for each stage of the manufacturing?

It will help if you do these things:
◆ list the stages in manufacturing
◆ plan the order of your manufacturing stages so that you save time or make production of quantities easier
◆ decide the details, e.g. measurements, colour, fit, etc. that would be best checked as you go along rather than after the whole product is finished.

It may help you to experiment, to find the best answers to some of these questions, before starting work on your product.

It may be useful to ask yourself:
◆ Does a particular process give a better appearance?
◆ Does a particular process make your product work better?
◆ Can savings be made by working in a particular way?

You can experiment with different ways to manufacture your product without having to make the whole thing. Check with your teacher first, to avoid waste, and keep a careful record of what you find out

You can then decide on:
◆ the best processes to use to make your product
◆ the best possible order for your manufacturing stages
◆ when to inspect and test for quality
◆ how to improve the quality of your product and reduce waste.

Carrying out production in school

Think of ways to design and make, or to use, **production aids** such as jigs, moulds, patterns and baking trays to improve the quality of your manufacturing.

You can also work with your classmates to increase your output and make more products faster.

Find out:
◆ What specialised equipment is available to you?
◆ Is it the same as manufacturing industry uses?
◆ If it is different, why is this?

Here are some processes that might be available in school which could be used to make products in quantity.

Vacuum-forming

In schools, formers are often made from solid materials such as MDF, or from mouldable materials such as Plasticine or clay. MDF is very suitable for making formers that will be used for producing items in quantity. Plasticine or clay is only really suitable for one-off production.

What common devices are used in producing a batch of food products to make sure that every one is the same size?

How could vacuum-formed objects be used with food for measured servings and making food shapes?

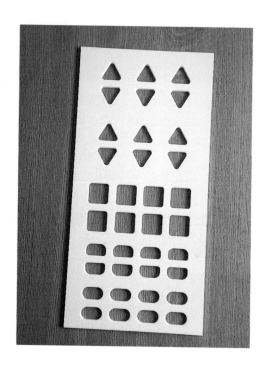

slight taper or draft.

MDF former made from layers glued together

A sophisticated former simply made from layers of MDF glued together. Note that all of the sides are cut to a draft angle

Making holes

Drilling is a common process and the pillar drills in industry are similar to those found in schools, although some industrial ones will drill several holes at one time. The problem with drilling is that whilst the machine will drill exactly the same hole every time, the material can move position. You can make simple production aids to ensure that the holes are always in the same place.

Green book:
Using jigs   122

Injection moulding

Injection moulding in industry involves very expensive tooling. In school, it is possible to produce injection moulded products using simple moulds that you can make yourself. There are three methods that you might consider depending upon the facilities in your school.

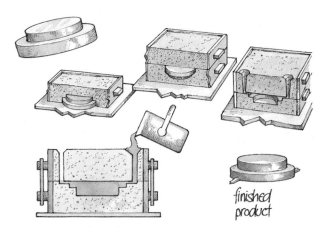

A wooden moulding pattern can be carefully made so that every product is the same

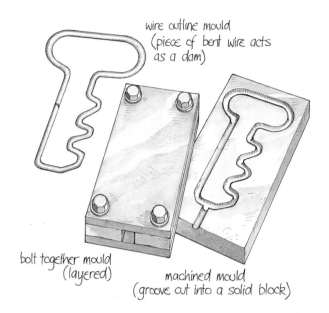

wire outline mould (piece of bent wire acts as a dam)

bolt together mould (layered)

machined mould (groove cut into a solid block)

Each of these moulds could be used in your school, depending upon the type of equipment that you have

What kinds of shapes are best made by using injection moulding? Is there any limit on their size?

Casting

Casting can be done in several ways depending upon the materials used. Aluminium and modern pewter are common metals that are used in schools. Other materials including food ingredients can also be cast or moulded.

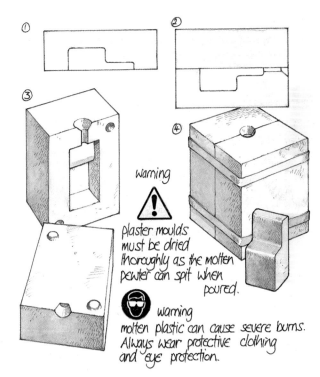

warning

plaster moulds must be dried thoroughly as the molten pewter can spit when poured.

warning
molten plastic can cause severe burns. Always wear protective clothing and eye protection.

A Plasticine form (or pattern) can be used to make the plaster of Paris mould. When set, the Plasticine is removed and the mould is thoroughly dried in an oven prior to pouring in the molten pewter

Red book:
Casting your jewellery   76

What products can you think of that are cast in moulds? What materials are their moulds made from?

Lathe turning

Lathes have been used for centuries to produce round products such as chair legs. This is called **turning**. The difficult part is ensuring that each one in a batch of products (e.g. four chair legs) is the same. This can be done in several ways.

Using a template. Matching the turning to the template needs considerable skill

Careful measurements must be taken if each product is to be the same

CAD/CAM offers the most reliable method of repeating designs accurately

What kinds of shapes are made with the lathe? Could you use this method?

Weaving and knitting

For many centuries, fabric products have been made in quantity through weaving and knitting. In the past this was done by hand from memory of traditional patterns or through detailed written instructions.

Making fabric in quantity in schools can be much easier if computerised looms are available

Knitting can be easier if machines are used. These can be hand or computer controlled

What is best, hand-knitted or machine-knitted? In what ways?

Embroidery

Embroidery is often used as part of the production of textile goods, often for decoration or labelling. It is very difficult to repeat designs accurately unless specialised equipment is used.

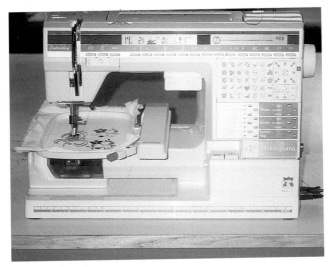

Programmable embroidery systems can help you to produce detailed designs that are the same every time

Which looks best, hand-made or programmed embroidery? Why?

Stamping and cutting sheet materials

Stamping shapes out of sheet materials is common in industry but not in schools. Other methods of cutting sheet materials in quantity might be available to you.

You may have cutting and stamping tools like these in your school

Thinking about volumes of production

Green book:
Making products in quantity 120

When you are planning to produce a number of items, you need to be clear about what you intend. Decide:
◆ Will your product be a model?
◆ Is it going to be a prototype?
◆ Is it going to be the real thing and put into use?
◆ How many identical products will you make?

Designing and manufacturing 'higher volumes' will mean:
1 Keeping things simple.

Millions of these cans have to be manufactured and each one must work perfectly. They have to be designed such that production is as reliable as possible

2 Choosing processes that are easy to repeat for the quantity needed.

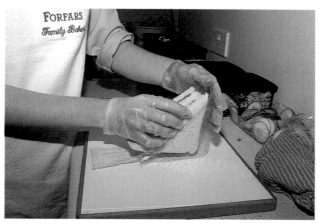

Lower volume batches of sandwiches being produced. Although more hand processes are used than for drinks cans, the sandwiches still have to be made reliably, efficiently and hygienically

3 Controlling the quality during production.

The monocycle is a one-off or 'made to measure' product for this rider, but the mountain bike has been manufactured in high volume. Both must work to the quality standards set during their manufacture

You must decide which aspects of your product need to be produced to what level of quality (**quality standard**) before you start manufacturing. How will you check these standards as you go along?

Using a specification to help your manufacturing

If you make quality checks during your manufacturing rather than just at the end, you are more likely to produce a high quality product.

Different kinds of specification may be used

Compare these two types of specification. What is each one for? How are they different?

Check these defects against the specifications shown. Which problems could have been avoided by using each specification properly?

Before manufacturing your product, draw up your own manufacturing specification and use it to check your work as you go along.

Planning the stages of manufacture in industry

When new kinds of products are developed in industry many things have to be planned and decided. This will include designing the layout of the factory spaces where the product is going to be made, and creating special tools and equipment to do different jobs as efficiently as possible.

Special tools are created and set out in order to manufacture shoes as efficiently as possible

Special tools can make jobs easier, placing less reliance on the skills of the workforce. Is this an advantage for the workers? Is this an advantage for the manufacturing company?

Factory layouts

See how the layout of this sandwich factory helps efficient production

In this factory they decided that:
◆ special machines would be needed to store and prepare the sandwich ingredients
◆ there was a best order for sandwich assembly stages
◆ equipment could be arranged to make assembly as quick and easy as possible
◆ the supply of bread and fillings could be specially arranged for speed
◆ the safety of the staff and the customers is always very important
◆ checking, at many stages, would be used to control quality.

TASK	DESCRIPTION	DISTANCE	RATE
○ ⇒ ■ ▽ ▷	Pass to line		
○ ⇒ ■ ▽ ▷	Butter bread		
○ ⇒ ■ ▽ ▷	Ham on bread		
○ ⇒ ■ ▽ ▷	Visual check		
○ ⇒ ■ ▽ ▷	Salad		
○ ⇒ ■ ▽ ▷	Top on sandwich		
○ ⇒ ■ ▽ ▷	Metal detection test		
○ ⇒ ■ ▽ ▷	Cut		
○ ⇒ ■ ▽ ▷	Pack		
○ ⇒ ■ ▽ ▷	Chill		
○ ⇒ ■ ▽ ▷	Boxing		
○ ⇒ ■ ▽ ▷	Storage		
○ ⇒ ■ ▽ ▷	Dispatched		

The sandwich manufacturing stages have been carefully planned so that they flow together as easily as possible

125

You should make a process flow chart for a part of your next product and ask yourself, can I think of ways to make the chart simpler or to reduce the number of stages? Will this improve the quality of manufacturing?

Working in teams in industry

It is very unusual for higher volumes to be created by one person because most workers have to do specialised jobs. They also have to avoid making too many or too few products at any one time. Too many will incur expensive warehouse costs, too few will mean frustrated customers. Have you ever wanted to buy something that was constantly 'out of stock'?

These boots have been over-produced for the time of year. To store them until the autumn could make them less profitable. Why?

Manufacturing needs teams

Green book:
Working in teams 109

Volume manufacturing often requires many people to be involved so they need to work together as a team. Members of a production team help each other by:

◆ carrying out different tasks, using the best person for each job
◆ keeping things moving and avoiding hold-ups
◆ keeping to time
◆ keeping to quality standards as they work
◆ thinking of ways to make improvements.

How well can you do these five things when making your D&T product?
◆ How can you best arrange your stages?

◆ How can you plan these to reduce delays and hold-ups?

◆ Are there any special tools or jigs that will help you to save time or improve quality?

◆ What kinds of quality checks are needed and when should you do them?

◆ What did you learn from your last D&T product and how will you improve your work this time?

Good teams produce the best products at prices people can afford

Index